Merchant Navy – What A Life

Merchant Navy
What A Life!

By Bob Jackman

Merchant Navy – What A Life

2nd Edition

Copyright © Bob Jackman 2013

Thanks to Phil Watson for all his help and expertise in publishing this book.

First edition published by Farthings Publishing in 2012

This edition published in Great Britain in 2013 by Bob Jackman

Cover design by Farthings Publishing

CONTENTS

Merchant Navy – What A Life

ALSO BY BOB JACKMAN
SHARK
Diverse Verses
Merchant Navy: Heroes & Half-wits
Merchant Navy: Retired

Merchant Navy – What A Life

Merchant Navy – What A Life

PREFACE

December 2011

I spent forty years of my life as an Engineer Officer in the Merchant Navy starting from the 21st June 1950 until I was invalided out in June 1990, a victim of high blood pressure.

But I have seen the wonders of New York from the top of the Statue of Liberty and walked through the horrors of Burlap Mansions in Bombay. I have twice had a fright from sharks and survived the 1956 typhoon 'Wanda' in an old tramp ship. I have slaved for fifty-one hours without a break in the broiling heat of an engine room; I have also served in immaculate engine rooms where it was a problem to find something to do to pass the time.

But my book is not just about places or events. This book of mine is more about the fellows of all ranks, of all departments on all the ships in the British Merchant Navy, whoever they may be.

God bless every damn one of them.

HOW IT ALL STARTED

I was born in a tenement in a back street in Glasgow in 1929 when unemployment raged through the whole of the United Kingdom. My father, like so many other men in those far-off days, spent the following seven years 'on the dole' and his only luxury was six pence for an ounce of the cheapest black bogie roll tobacco for his pipe, once a week. I can clearly remember one week when my father didn't take his tobacco money because he said it would soon be Christmas and my mother would need the money to buy presents for my sister and me.

In those days, mothers watched every penny and that era was well named 'The Depression.'

In his struggle against inactivity and boredom, I remember my dad doing experiments, simple science with bottles and tubes and similar items. I was mesmerised when he made water flow up a tube or when he broke the bottom off a bottle, replaced it with the bottle top inside and no one could see the join. He made 'Frog' model type aeroplanes out of hard cardboard that were powered by elastic bands. He once put an electric motor and battery into a tin boat he had made. A lovely job but the motor was too heavy and it sank. All simple science to him but it was magic to me, a four-year old boy.

Merchant Navy – What A Life

My earliest toy I can remember was a type of 'Meccano' set called 'Trix'. It was a box of metal girders of various dimensions, some straight, some angled, wheels of different diameters and packets of tiny bolts and nuts. My 'Trix' was added to every Christmas and every birthday by relatives and friends – they knew what I always appreciated as the years went by.

'Trix' was the incentive that inspired my interest in everything of a technical or scientific nature. I built cars and cranes and all kinds of gadgets in my childhood days.

In my secondary school days in the war years, with fifty-one in the class, I was always in the top three in Science, Mathematics and Technical subjects. Be that as it may, my only real claim to fame on any subject was on History. I scored a mere 9% in a finals history exam. School records, going back through to the early days when the school was first built, showed that no one ever had a mark as low as 9% on any subject in any exam in any year.

I left school at fourteen and at fifteen started serving my full five years apprenticeship in Barclay Curle's Marine Engine Works on the Clyde. For five years I had to do an early morning dash by tramcars from Possilpark in the north of Glasgow to Whiteinch in the far west of Glasgow followed by rushing to evening classes in the centre of the city three nights a week. Many apprentices struggled through this hardship but staggering to the evening classes after a hard day slogging in a Clydeside engine works was too much for some.

In my first year in the Engine Works I earned twenty-four shillings (£1.20p) per week when I had pals earning £7.00 per week leisurely shovelling coal in the Springburn Railway yards. If it started to rain they settled themselves in one of the railway wagons and played cards until the rain stopped. In the shipyards if it started to rain, you got wet.

Again, in shipbuilding, this being the war years, many were called up for the armed services and a second year apprentice could serve his two or three or even four years military service and found when he was returned to the engine works he was still just a second year apprentice with a second year apprentice's wages.

If an apprentice was caught with a can of tea during working hours he was sacked on the spot. Taking a few days off for no apparent reason? Goodbye. A fist fight? They sacked both combatants, regardless of who started the fight or what the fight was about.

On one occasion I pointed out to a forty-year-old ragged idiot that he was standing on a valve on top of the boiler fuel pump and his foot was bending the valve spindle.

I was seventeen and very much an apprentice.

He was furious. 'You ***** ***. Who do you think you are talking to? I'm going to see you

4

round behind the ****** plumbers shed and I will ****** knock your head off!!!!!!'

He was a nothing, an ignoramus only fit for the most menial tasks. I, on the other hand, cherished my job and my future, but could I back down? Or run away and hide?

He went round all the workers and told them he was going to murder a ****** apprentice that had given him cheek. He gathered an audience to show what he could do.

To me, there was no hiding place.

I arrived and waited for him. My lunch 'pieces' lay in my jacket pocket beside the plumbers shed. I was too nervous to eat them and afraid I might be sick.

'Here he comes, laddie. You could be OK.'

'Never seen him fight before.'

'Looks the wiry type.'

So the workers made a circle around us and my opponent made a show of taking off his jacket then looked at me with a contemptuous sneer on his face. He threw a few punches in the air to loosen his muscles and impress his workmates.

We approached each other, fists up, ready for battle. He bobbed and weaved, then moved in close to clobber me.

But I hit him first! It wasn't really much of a punch, more of a hefty push on the side of his face and it wouldn't have been hard enough to bring tears to the eyes of a ten-year old boy.

But he went down! He lay on his side on the ground with one hand raised to defend himself in case I was going to hit him again.

'OK! OK! You win, I've had enough, you win, you win. All finished, you win, don't hit me any more.'

If any foreman had come round the corner of the plumbers' shed at that moment, my career in marine engineering would have been over.

I still rage when I think about it - and that was over sixty-five years ago.

And I still remember many of the great men I worked with in those days in the late 1940s, great men that taught me so much yet they were not obliged to teach me anything. So many master craftsmen who were quite nonchalant about their capabilities, and to me, nearly every one is a hero.

In 1950 I left Barclay Curle's Marine Engine Works in Whiteinch, Glasgow, with a paper to briefly state I was a time-served Clydeside engine fitter. Two days later I joined my first ship in Liverpool, the MV Marjata, as Fifth Engineer Officer and that was the start of my career in the British Merchant Navy. I remember struggling up the gangway with my big suitcase and clambering into the alleyway correctly assuming it to be the entrance to the engineers' accommodation. The Chief Engineer was just coming out of his cabin and, as he locked his cabin door, he looked up and saw me.

'You're the new Fiver?'

'Yes, sir.'

He snorted. 'We don't say 'sir' on board these ships.'

'Yes, sir.'

He shook his head and sighed. 'Get into your uniform, the dinner gong will be ringing in a minute. That's your cabin at the end of the pantry.'

My cabin had a bunk with two drawers, a settee with two drawers, a desk with two drawers and a chair that dominated the centre of the cabin. There was also a wardrobe barely twelve inches wide, a washhand basin and a mirror. So, this was home, sweet home for a Merchant Navy Fifth Engineer Officer in the many months to follow and it didn't have enough floor space to include a ship's cat.

I threw open my suitcase, put on my brand new uniform and found my way to the officers' dining saloon.

The saloon consisted of two tables, one for engineer officers, one for deck officers, with the Chief Engineer and the Captain at the head of their respective tables. The Second, Third and Fourth Engineers sat in chairs down the inboard side of the engineers' table and I was obliged to sit at the end of the long settee facing the Fourth Engineer. They whispered among themselves as the two Indian stewards served the tables and eyes would sometimes flicker briefly in my direction.

Eventually, one of the Indian stewards condescended to fill my water glass, hand me the menu and take my order.

Apart from the whispering, the clink of cutlery and the gentle purring of the steam generator five decks below, the silence was deafening. I was the new boy, the first-tripper and they wouldn't want to know anything about me until I had proved myself.

A little fly circled my head and it didn't choose to ignore me as it did my fellow officers. It zoomed among the table ware and then landed on the rim of my water glass. One nonchalant swipe from me knocked my glass of water up the table to land on the Chief Engineer's roast beef and Yorkshires.

However, the days that followed were not quite as bad.

THE DANCE

The 'City of Chester' was a twin-screw vessel with two four-cylinder Doxford marine engines. The space between the two main engines was about twelve feet by thirty and space in an engine room was a rarity in most ships. On long sea trips when everything in an engine room is ticking over sweetly, boredom can set in and curing it is difficult. My junior assistant, Andy, told me so many times he was a gold medallist in ballroom dancing and he loved to show me some of its finer points, by dancing and twirling around in the large space between the engines.

The year was 1953, I was Fourth Engineer, Andy was Sixth Engineer, our watch was the twelve to four and we were both in our early twenties. He always grudged the fact that I was Fourth Engineer and he was not.

If I told him to do something, he would look at me, his body would sag and he would shake his head in disbelief. I often had to tell him twice in a louder voice and then had to check that he had carried out my orders. But if the Second Engineer spoke to him, he would stand, bewildered like a whipped puppy, as if more than his feelings had been hurt and everyone was bullying him.

He was, however, a real 'wally' in many ways. Like the time in the engine room workshop together when he squirted oil at my back then looked away as if he had nothing to do with it and the oil had come from somewhere else. I picked up an oil can on the bench where I was working and I knew it was full because of the weight of it. I clicked the trigger three or four times rapidly to make it sound as if the oil can was empty and he approached, with a smirk on his face with his oilcan at the ready. We did not behave like adults. I soaked him.

Or when we stopped in Ceuta, North Africa, to discharge some cargo and a native salesman came on board selling boots and shoes. His engine room shoes looked quite acceptable and very cheap so most of us bought a pair. Within a month the soles had worn through and the heels were falling off. One day, in port, I was duty engineer so I found some trivial jobs to do in the engine room rather than sit in my cabin.

I decided that repairing the soles and heels of my worn engine room shoes was a priority. At sea, I had made a cobbler's last of sorts, so I took a piece of old pulley belting, used nails from a tin box that hoarded hundreds of different sizes and types and I successfully soled and heeled my engine room shoes: A very satisfactory job.

Andy's shoes were in a worse condition than mine, so, even though he disliked most of us intensely and me in particular, my feelings for him were negligible, because he was a twit that should never have left home. I began to repair his shoes.

His shoe repairs were nearing completion when he came down the engine room and entered the work shop. He stood close and gently leaned against me, hoping no doubt, for an opportunity to nudge me accidentally, of course, as I was swinging the

hammer. So I stopped.

'Yes, Andy?'

'The Second wants you to start number two generator and knock off number three generator.'

'Thank you, Andy,' I smiled and went down below to carry out our Second Engineer's orders. About ten minutes later the generators were changed over and I returned to find Andy nonchalantly knocking two-inch nails into the soles and heels of his shoes.

The smirk on his face said: 'What are you going to do about it?'

I shrugged my shoulders and quietly rummaged in the nail box to find more two-inch nails for him. When he had bashed them in too, I picked up my beautifully repaired shoes from under the work-shop bench and showed them to him.

'You shouldn't have used two-inch nails in your shoes, Andy. I only used half-inch nails in mine.'

I watched the smirk slide off his face to be replaced by a look of dismay.

Our first port in America was New York, a city with a thousand wonderful sights: Broadway, The Statue of Liberty, 42nd Street, the Marine Club in the Astor Hotel, Jack Dempsey's Bar – the list is endless.

Our last port in America was San Francisco.

As always in America, padres from the Missions to Seamen or similar, would pay us a visit and give us a talk and an invitation to local organisations they recommended. Some of us chose one called 'The Ladies Auxiliary', and found it to be a Marine Club run by two elderly women with frigid and rigid rules. Chairs were arranged in a circle in the small mission hall and we were requested to sit in every second chair. Secondly, when the girls arrived en masse ten minutes later, they sat themselves in the alternate chairs. After five minutes a little bell tinkled and the girls moved up a space. But the girls were friendly and becoming friendlier as the minutes went past. Our future looked bright.

Then the highlight of the evening began. The girls left their chairs to go to a table prepared by the old ladies and returned with two tea plates containing cream crackers heavily spread with peanut butter and topped with strawberry jam. We were also presented with a teabag in a cup of hot water. No sugar, no milk, no teaspoon.

'We know it's just the way your mothers make it for you, back in England', the two elderly hostesses simpered. 'We don't want you to get homesick, though.'

The lovely creature sitting beside me and breathing gently in my ear whispered. 'We have never known any English boys who ate crackers spread with peanut butter and strawberry jam back home in England.'

'We don't eat them in Scotland either.'

Her lovely dark eyes widened. 'You're Scotch?'

'I am Scottish. Scotch is a drink loved by the Scots.'

Her eyes lit up, she gazed deeply into mine and I now had difficulty breathing. 'Could you and two of your friends meet three of us outside at the corner of 23rd and Beaver? There's a bar we would love to take you to. Have you two Scotch friends here?'

'Yes.'

Eventually the meeting came to an end and house rules demanded that the young ladies said their goodbyes and left fifteen minutes before the boys.

I asked the impossible Andy if he would like to be one of our group of three.

'Go anywhere with you, a Scotsman? Not on your life.'

Gerry O'Hare, Bill Cox, 'Muscles' Manson, Jimmy Hudson and others jumped at the chance. I didn't need to ask any of them twice but I kept our limit to three as my young lady requested.

Our obnoxious Andy had a parting shot at me as we left. 'You know what they say about Scotsmen.'

So it came to pass that my choice was Gerry O'Hare, Jimmy Hudson and me.

We found the girls at the corner of 23rd and Beaver as agreed and they led us all the way to this '555 Club'. It was called the '555 Club' because that was its street number on 23rd Street but the sign above the entrance said 'The Little Bit of Scotland.'

We took a vacant table on the far side. There was a small stage and a woman was singing Scottish Songs with a heavy American accent while her partner played the piano in accompaniment.

A waitress came to take our order. Her notebook was ready, her pencil was poised, and her gum was temporarily shifted to the right side of her mouth.

'Yeah?'

'Six beers, please.'

My girl watched the waitress's face. 'Bob is Scottish.'

The waitress nodded. 'They all say that.' Her mouth returned to slow motion on her chewing gum. 'Yeah? Say murder.'

When she said it, it sounded more like 'moider' than 'murder.'

'No moider, lassie, it is 'murder' and I can also say it's a braw bricht moonlit nicht the nicht as weel.'

She looked at me for a long minute then disappeared through the crowd and came back clutching a piece of paper to her chest. Her attitude had changed.

'Ok, guy, let me ask you two questions. Let's see if you are Scotch.' She was now very serious and the bar had gone quiet. I gathered that this was a procedure that the bar was noted for and the prize had never been won in many years if at all.

'I am Scottish.'

'Yeah. Sure.' She studied her piece of paper. 'What was the most famous battle ever fought in Scotland?'

'The Battle of Bannockburn, 1314, where the Scots under Robert the Bruce defeated the English.'

The singing had fizzled out, the piano was no longer playing and the bar was now deadly quiet.

'Good. Yeah, 1314, you got that right. Okay, Scotchman, now here is the all-important question. That was the Robert the Bruce fellow, yeah. But answer this. Who was De Bohun?' She spoke softly but clearly and her fist was gripping the paper tightly to her ample bosom. Two more waitresses had silently joined her.

It didn't sound as if anyone was breathing. 'De Bohun was a French mercenary on the English side, mounted on his charger and in full armour. He charged Bruce before the battle started and Bruce took his head clean off with one swipe of his jackman's axe.'

She was stunned! She stood motionless for at least half a minute, then she spun round and waved the crumpled paper at the customers. 'That's right! This Scotchman gave the right answer! Drinks are on the house. Everybody, have what you like! Clear the centre table, make space for these guys.'

She turned to me and our faces were inches apart. 'My ancestors were the De Bohuns from Lille in France and Simon de Bohun was killed in a battle in Scotland in 1314! You sure got it right!'

We were ushered to the large table in the centre of 'The Little Bit of Scotland' with the customers cheering and pushing each other to pat me on the back. A litre bottle of Dalwhinnie 15 Year Old Single Malt Whisky was ceremoniously brought to the table on a silver tray and all our glasses were filled.

That I took no ice in my whisky surprised the customers. Because I didn't do it, they didn't do it. Everything had to be Scottish that night. Even I got up on the stage, sang a couple of Scottish songs and many joined in. An hour later we were all still in full voice when two cops came in through the door, one white and one black.

'Right, you guys! What in the hell is going on here? You know your licence ends at midnight.'

Before our hosts could speak, I faced the two policemen. It has been said that Dalwhinnie Malt gives the Scots terrific courage.

Merchant Navy – What A Life

'Gentlemen, I am a born and bred Scotsman and every brave American policeman I know has Scottish grandparents or Scottish great grandparents in their history somewhere. Would you care to drink to your ancestry in Scotland's greatest whisky?'

They looked at each other for a moment then the white one said, 'Waal, I just know I sure got a Scotch grandmother somewhere. Yeah, I remember my mother telling me that when I was a kid.' He took the two glasses offered and handed one to his black partner.

'Well, what do you know?' His partner took the glass. 'You'se got a Scotch grandmama? Then I reckons I'se sure got one somewhere too.'

We were there, they were there, everybody was still there until three o'clock in the morning, laughing and singing, and finally the three of us ended up in someone's car that took us back to the good ship, MV 'City of Chester'.

Of course Andy, the sixth engineer, my mate on watch, being his usual repulsive self, complained bitterly to everybody on board that we were mates on watch and I hadn't invited him to go with us to 'The Little Bit of Scotland.'

We sailed from San Francisco to New Zealand, and when there was hardly a ripple on the water during the calm days, Andy turned to practising his ballroom dancing in the space between the engines. He became so engrossed in his dance steps that he often took me as his dancing partner, much to the total astonishment of our Indian crew.

In my home town of Glasgow, young lads began their dancing days in ballrooms like the Locarno, Green's Playhouse, the Denniston Palais and others but as their dancing ability improves over the years, some graduate to 'The Albert.' No disrespect to the others, but 'The Albert's clientele stood well above those in every dance hall within five hundred miles and being with the elite made you want to be their equal. You improved by watching and following the movements of the experts.

Andy had been taught by teachers and understood the various terms that sounded like 'sashey','re-swan' and dozens of others I had forgotten by the time we had come off watch.

After the long haul across the Pacific we arrived in Lytteleton, New Zealand. Five minutes after we had arrived, a Mission to Seamen padre was on board inviting us to a dance at his local mission, starting at seven o'clock that evening.

Everyone under the age of forty was interested and those in their early twenties were even more interested so we arrived in good time.

The mission hall had a row of young ladies seated down one side of the hall and a row of young gentlemen seated down the opposite side of the hall. A five piece orchestra was playing a Strauss waltz.

Something I learned many years ago in the world of dancing was to look at the girls' shoes. Those that wear proper dance shoes are dancers. That your intended partner is the correct height is another point to be considered.

She filled those two requirements but she was also very beautiful. A mere wisp that floated like part of a wonderful dream and our bodies were never more than a millimetre apart. Andy had shown me many advanced steps and we did them like two professionals who had been practising for months.

We were the only couple on the floor; the others were now on their feet to watch our every movement.

The obnoxious Andy was in the front line judging every move we made, his mouth twisted in anger and derision.

On the music's finishing notes, I swung this young lady in a series of reverse whisks to the centre of the hall, placed my right hand in the small of her back and arched her slender body backwards until her hair touched the floor. But I bent her one millimetre too far, I fell over her and we crashed to the floor. Everybody applauded, whistled, stamped their feet and cheered like mad. I heard Andy's laughter above all others.

That was in 1955 and in my memory I can hear that blighter laughing yet.

Damn him!

NO STAND-BY

The main engine on the 'M.V. Megna' was a three cylinder economy Doxford, a sweet, dependable unit that was very popular back in the 1940s and 50s. The seawater, fresh water cooling and lubricating oil pumps were driven off the main engine when she was running at sea, but were powered by steam driven pumps during 'stand-bys' when the main engines were slowed or stopped. It took time to change over from one system to the other and required the services of two Engineers.

When nearing a port, it was required that one hour's notice was given by the Captain or the deck officer on the bridge to allow the Engineers to change over the pumps for 'stand-by.' However, on the 'Megna', there were those, one Captain and one First Mate, two 'half- wits' that shall remain nameless, who sometimes 'forgot' to give the one hour's notice, and 'forgot' to ring 'Stand-by' and would, instead, ring 'Slow Ahead' or 'Stop.'

With only one engineer in the engine room, no chance to call for assistance, no pumps changed over, air bottles shut, air compressors off and 'Slow Ahead' on the telegraph, it caused pure pandemonium and blind panic for the Engineer on watch. If he slowed the main engine, the pumps could lose suction and the main engine would then be without sea water or fresh water cooling or lubrication oil to the bearings.

When the hierarchy of the deck department were confronted by our outraged Chief Engineer, they smiled knowingly at each other, gave their brief apologies and dismissed the matter. To them, it was funny, because they pictured the ship's engineers in a panic like a Walt Disney cartoon movie. They did it a few times.

Then came one wonderful day when we changed Chief Engineers. Harry, our new Chief, was a man we all looked up to in two ways. One, he was a six-foot-six-inch Australian that smiled easily and hailed from a place called Cassowary Creek, up in the right hand corner of Australia somewhere. And two, he was an excellent Chief Engineer.

At mealtimes in the saloon, the Captain and the Mate engaged our new Chief Engineer in conversation, just to find out what kind of man this new Chief Engineer was, and of course, they found him extremely pleasant and agreeable in all matters. We, the engineers, also found him extremely pleasant and agreeable in all matters.

Bill Underwood, our Second Engineer, ran a tidy engine room where everything functioned well. All maintenance work was carried out to his satisfaction and routine overhauls kept everything in good working order. Anything that was used was entered in the Spare Gear Book or anything that was needed was entered in the

Stores Book. Bill kept his work book up to date and he was not a writer of fiction. But he raged at the engine room telegraph business, to no avail.

Gordon Thomson, the Third Engineer and Electrician was an easy fellow to get on with, but he disliked half-wits. He often recalls the time when the Mate came back to the ship after a night ashore in Liverpool. 'It was one o'clock on a dirty wet morning when the Mate came into my cabin as drunk as a monkey, woke me up, and told me his bunk light wouldn't switch off and how was he supposed to get a night's sleep when his bunk light was lit? What was I going to do about it? We went to his cabin; I unscrewed the bulb in his bunk light, handed it to him and went back to my bed without saying a word.'

I was Fourth Engineer and one of those obnoxious characters that are too fond of engineers, engines and engineering to be popular with lesser mortals in the deck department.

Our Fifth Engineer was John Patrick Bernard Aloisys Ignacious Quintus McMahon who answered to the name of 'Charlie'. He had been a Junior Engineer for a long, long time and would continue to be a Junior Engineer for many more years to come.

So we left Liverpool in the UK and our first port was Durban, South Africa. When we arrived, no one hour's notice given from the bridge and the telegraph suddenly rang, 'Dead Slow Ahead.'

Our new, smiling Chief Engineer Officer just happened to be on one of his rare visits to the engine room at that moment and I, Fourth Engineer Officer, was on my 8 to 12 watch.

'Let's go look at the stern gland, Bob,' he smiled, ignoring the telegraph's order from the bridge for 'Dead Slow Ahead.'

So with him leading the way, we strolled down the shaft tunnel, casually checking each shaft bearing until we reached the aforementioned stern gland.

He nodded his head in satisfaction. 'Stern gland seems OK to me. Are you happy with it, Bob?'

'If you are happy with it, Chief, then I am happy with it, too.'

'Good. Now let's walk back to the engine room and see what else we can be happy about.'

The Second, Third and Fifth Engineers were dashing round the engine room like outraged hens, trying to get the sea water and fresh water steam pumps started, and trying to open all main engine air bottle master valves.

Our three cylinder economy Doxford was still on full revs.

The First Mate was hanging over the handrail on the top platform of the main engine, frantically screaming his head off, jumping up and down and no one was paying the slightest bit of attention to him.

The engine room telegraph was ringing all kinds of hysterical orders from the bridge but none were being answered by the engineers.

Eventually it was all over. The Captain had raced the 'Megna' up the narrow channel into the highly congested Durban Bay at full sea revs, did an about turn in the bay, missed other ships by a few feet and raced down the channel into the open sea again.

Ships' horns, hooters, whistles and sirens squealed, blasted and roared at us and our Captain was on the bridge in a blind panic, screaming like a madman.

Finally our steam pumps were started; engine-driven pumps were shut down, air bottles were opened, air compressors now running and our three cylinder economy Doxford main engine was slowed to Dead Slow Ahead.

It took over an hour, half a bottle of tranquilisers and a few large whiskies before the Captain stopped crying. Similar medication stopped the Mate's shaking and they were both were now sufficiently recovered to take the 'M.V.Megna' into Durban at 'Dead Slow Ahead.'

We were invaded by angry shore side authorities and senior officers from other ships who came storming on board demanding explanations and the arguments went on for the rest of the afternoon.

Harry was there and some of the authorities were not ships' Captains.

Harry, Chief Engineer Officer, from Cassowary Creek in Australia was a nice guy that smiled easily, but when he spoke, people listened.

'This has happened before on this type of ship. A Burmese ship called the 'MV Garanda'. There was no hour's notice from the bridge, just a sudden 'Dead Slow Ahead'. The engineers raced like mad to get the steam pumps warmed through and running and the main engine pumps shut down but in the mad dashing around a main sea water discharge valve happened to be left shut. With the main engine still running the main sea water pump casing burst and killed the Fourth Engineer. This could have happened again here this morning, on this ship. I shall be taking the matter up with the Board of Trade, the Merchant Navy Union and our shipping company's solicitors. I suggest you do the same.'

So it came to pass that Bill Underwood, Gordon Thomson, John Patrick Bernard Aloisys Quintus McMahon and I were wedged into the duty mess having a beer when Harry walked in.

Bill asked him. 'Hey, Chief, what was the name of the ship where the engineer got killed by the sea water pump exploding?'

'Can't remember.'

'Or the name of the engineer?' Gordon asked him quietly.

He gazed at the deck head. 'Oh! Funny I can't remember that either. I think maybe I should have left it all to Bob. He tells better stories than I do.'

Be that as it may, from that day, engine room staff were always formally given a one hour's notice of 'Stand By' because when Harry spoke, people listened. Especially Captains.

FIRST TRIP SECOND

I sat and passed all the exams required for my Second's Ticket and my status immediately soared from being a mere Fourth Engineer Officer to the dizzy heights of Certificated Second Engineer Officer.

It always puzzled me that out of the forty-one entrants that sat the exams in Glasgow only a few of us passed, yet I knew many of them to be highly competent, time-served engineers that had spent many hard months studying. At lunch time, we had a pub lunch and a pint in the Carlton Bar next door to the college and over our pie and chips we discussed thermodynamics, electro-technology, naval architecture, refrigeration and other subjects concerned with marine engineering.

Even Old Willie, who had been the bartender in the Carlton Bar since he was a teenager, could answer some of the technical questions likely to be found in exam papers and he had never even been in a ship's engine room.

This was our world.

At home, I would have either of my parents open any of my many text books and read the first few lines on a page chosen at random. I would continue from where they left off. I didn't read it parrot fashion but I could give the facts on that subject on that page. John

Lamb was my hero and his 'Running and Maintenance of the Marine Diesel Engine' was my bible. I also read every one of his other publications on marine auxiliaries and other allied subjects. Every one of us in McGibbons College studied books by Sothern, C.C.Pounder, and McGibbon's own excellent books.

Many of us owe a huge debt to Mr James Holburn and Mr Hugh Barr, the two highly qualified principals of McGibbon's College of Marine Engineering in Glasgow, for their teaching abilities and their patience.

Yet there was a shortage of qualified engineer officers in 1956, but why? And why were some of the Chiefs I sailed with so incompetent? Incompetent? Some were idiots!

I joined my first ship as Second Engineer but I probably still thought and acted like a Fourth Engineer and this caused me a lot of grief. Five years as an apprentice in Barclay Curle's Diesel Engine Works on Doxford engines, then sailing with them for a further six years gave me a lot of knowledge on these engines. Evening classes at Glasgow High School during my apprenticeship years and two three month sessions at McGibbon's College of Marine Engineering earned me my BOT Certificate Second Class. I passed all seven subjects on my first attempt. That was a full eleven years experience in Doxford engines and crazy as it may sound, I loved the damned things.

I still have my references as Fifth and Fourth Engineer in those early 1950s and there isn't a bad one among them.

My problems began as Second with the first Chief Engineer I sailed with, whose lack of knowledge was appalling and many marine engineers reading this will agree. I list some of his shortcomings:

1) T&K cylinder lubricators were set to pump in six times the amount of lubricating oil they were designed for. He confused the amount per watch with the amount per day and would not be told otherwise. Sight glasses burst and I replaced them with steel tubing when we soon run out of spare glasses. Cylinder oil must have been streaming down the cylinder walls, into the scavenge spaces and being one of the main causes of our continuous spate of scavenge fires.

2) New fuel valve spray plates were locked away. He gave orders to the Fourth Engineer overhauling fuel valves to use old spray plates. To his way of thinking, worn holes on fuel valves allowed more fuel into the cylinders, therefore more power. But, where it should have been a fine spray, fuel streamed into the cylinders and ran down the cylinder walls with the cylinder oil into the scavenge spaces.

3) Before I joined, when re-ringing main engine pistons, he permitted the Indian crew to file the piston ring grooves. The grooves on the pistons on the Megna were then no longer parallel and piston rings broke into pieces when

the engine was running. My arguments went unheeded.

4) Three heavy oil purifiers/clarifiers were installed fourteen inches apart, in one tiny room cut into upper tank flat. The heat was oppressive and the fumes made your eyes smart. One day, the centre purifier screamed to a halt when its internal gearing froze and shattered. The Fourth Engineer and I were fitting new parts and suddenly the second purifier screamed to a halt. It was only by chance that we found that the Indian greasers and donkeymen were using the purifier/clarifier clean oil storage tank as a waste oil tank. The Indian engine room Serang wept that he was obeying the Chief's orders and the Chief evaded all my questions when I approached him on the subject.

I had joined the ship as fit as a pit bull terrier, but constantly working a sixteen hour day in those conditions caused my first heart attack. A twentysix-year old with a heart attack? Since we carried twelve passengers we also carried a doctor and this little man jumped up and down in sheer frustration at my heart condition and the hours I worked. I was still working a sixteen hour day every day since I joined. Number one diesel generator wiped its bearings and contributed to my second heart attack - but it didn't stop me working.

I gripped the Chief by his lapels, pushed my nose to within six inches of his and explained in detail what he was doing wrong - but to no avail. He wouldn't look at me. His eyes never made contact with mine. He never listened to a single word I said.

We docked in Liverpool in October 1956. It was January 1957 before I was fit enough to join another ship.

But what if I had sent a letter to Head Office stating those facts? To all Second Engineers in those circumstances, I would recommend sending one copy to Head Office, one copy for the Chief Engineer himself and one copy for the Engine room workbook. I would not have ended up a shattered wreck or a suitable candidate for a shore side loony bin if I had done so.

All the Chief Engineers I sailed with after him agreed with me completely. It's what they would have done in these circumstances.

When I did return to sea I was quite a different person. I dared anyone, from the Captain down to the second cook aft, to step out of line with me in any way. It is an old adage at sea that if you are Second Engineer you are either a bad bastard or a stupid bastard. I had been a stupid bastard – through my youth and inexperience. Now I quietly seethed with an internal fury. I was now a bad bastard. It was my second ship as Second Engineer Officer and I had a different Chief.

Months later, it was New Year's Eve when we arrived in San Francisco for twenty-four hours and found we had a cracked bottom piston in number two unit.

I told the Chief and we looked at each other without speaking. We both knew it had to be changed, but we also knew it was New Year's Eve and the engineers, me included, were Scots.

'We'll do it, Chief, tonight.'

So I went to the smoke room where the engineers were getting things ready to celebrate the coming of 1982 at midnight.

'Number two unit has a cracked bottom piston and we are sailing tomorrow. I'm going to put on my boilersuit and go down to start dismantling it. I'll need a hand.'

By the time I had my boiler suit on and heading for the engine room door there were six engineers and one electrician following me. The bottom piston was changed in record time and we were all back in the smoke room minutes before midnight.

We were very pleased with us. And, quietly, I was terribly proud of that squad of engineers.

I've had many great Chiefs and other ranks of engineers as these stories will verify. Many are named in my books and I would gladly give a month's pay to sail with them again. Chief Engineer's personal references are beside me in my desk drawer as I write and I sometimes take them out, read them and memories come flooding back to me, hence these stories.

Yes, I repeat that I would cheerfully give a month's pay to be granted the opportunity to sail with any of them again but I'll be eighty-three next birthday.

Merchant Navy – What A Life

I remember them all.

THE MONEY MAN

He joined in Calcutta and from that first day he never spoke to any of us if he could possibly avoid it. When he passed any of us in an alleyway or on deck it was as if he was passing a pedestrian in a busy street in an unknown town. A wise man once said of a politician: 'He doesn't have an enemy in the world and none of his friends like him.' This expression fitted our new First Mate to perfection.

Probably in his mid-fifties, well-made physically but his face was quite devoid of expression at all times.

From Calcutta, we sailed to Madras, Colombo and Capetown and then took the long haul across the Atlantic to Trinidad. I remember it was a Saturday, the engineers were younger than me and were long overdue a break so I knocked them all off for the weekend while I did the duty on board. I was now in my fifties and shoreside delights were no longer a temptation. With my feet up, a good book in my hand, I was at peace with the world.

Then suddenly there were voices and footsteps and these distracted me because there was only the Mate and me on board. However, that was the Mate's department; my department was strictly the engine room and all matters of a technical nature if something went wrong.

It came to pass that this weird Mate with the blank expression and who rarely spoke to anyone, appeared in my doorway. 'I want you to come and witness my signature on a document.'

I didn't like him and I certainly didn't like his manner so I went back to reading my book. 'Come back on Monday. Maybe I'll witness your signature then.'

The air was static for a few minutes before he spoke again. 'There are two government officials who have flown from Heathrow to Trinidad to get my signature on an important government document. It has to be confirmed and counter-signed by an officer on board the ship.'

Normally, in circumstances like this, you'll oblige any shipmate without question but he had always insisted on being an awkward ass so I could be one too. I had made my point so I took my feet off my desk and stood up. 'OK, lead me to your bits of paper.'

There were two bureaucratic types seated in his cabin and they seemed pleasant but nervous and they watched his every move. They fussed about with a couple of official documents that the Mate signed. Then I was handed the pen and I signed my name under his signatures.

They bowed. 'Thank you, gentlemen, we must go now. We have a taxi waiting.'

They shook hands with us and left in a hurry.

I turned to face the Mate. 'This intrusion on my privacy in off-duty hours costs you a beer. Now, what in the hell was that all about?'

He stared at his feet with his hands behind his back and seemed to be making up his mind about something. Suddenly he unlocked a cupboard, took out a beer lying there and handed it to me. Then he locked the cupboard again and put the key in his pocket. He didn't offer me a bottle opener.

He cleared his throat. 'They want me to spread my hens' eggs over the fields so they won't get wasted.'

Did I hear him right?

I repeated his words slowly. 'They want you to spread your hens' eggs over the fields so they won't get wasted?'

He nodded. His eyes looked a bit funny and I thought the unopened bottle of beer could be quite handy in an emergency.

'Who wants you to spread what hens' eggs over what field?'

'It's because the government wants Poland to have two destroyers built in Tyneside.'

I was beginning to feel things were not right in the Mate's head, and icy fingers ran up and down my spine. My eyes measured the distance from where I was sitting to the cabin door.

I think he began to sense my discomfort. 'Maybe I could explain it better. You see, my sister is younger than me. There were seven of us and Grandfather's investment came to me when he died. I actually preferred the two brass candle sticks that always stood on his mantelpiece but she wanted them and I let her have them and I got his investment shares.

My brothers and sisters that were older than me were left the rest of his stuff, but Gaynor, my sister, got the two brass candlesticks and I got Grandfather's investment shares.'

'Yeah, you said that.'

'You see, Grandfather was left some money from a woman he knew and shouldn't have known, if you see what I mean. He didn't think it was right that he should have it so someone told him to invest it somewhere far away and it would eventually just frizzle away to nothing. But he invested it in an Australian company called 'Broken Hill Proprieties' and the amount got bigger, not smaller.'

I had heard of Broken Hill Proprieties. It's the biggest and most profitable company in all Australia.

'And?'

'Well, it gave me enough to buy a farm; a farm with enough land to raise chickens and cows. Yes, and horses. And Gaynor got the brass candlesticks. Gaynor is my young sister. Not pigs, they stank too much. I don't like pigs.'

I was getting exasperated. 'You've already said that! You got the farm, Gaynor got the brass candlesticks. What did the others get from your Grandfather's investment? Did they get anything?'

He thought for a moment. 'Well Garret, my oldest brother, got my grandfather's gold watch. It didn't work, though. Never worked in years but Grandfather wouldn't part with it. The others just signed some lawyers' papers to say they didn't want anything to do with grandfather's investment and I wanted the brass candlesticks and Gaynor wanted the brass candlesticks so we signed different lawyers' papers. And Gaynor was always nice to me so I let her ....'

I exploded. 'Yes! She got the candlesticks! You've told me that about ten bliddy times! And you got the farm. What else? You said something about Poland wanting two destroyers built on the Tyne....'

'Yes.'

'Yes, WHAT?'

'Yes, I was London's biggest egg supplier. If I stopped my eggs to London the government would buy eggs from Poland and the money Poland got from our government buying their eggs would help them to pay for the two destroyers to be built on the Tyne.'

My brains were in turmoil. I couldn't grasp any of it. His farm was the biggest supplier of eggs to London? He was helping the government assist Poland to pay for two destroyers to be built on the Tyne? He had wanted the two brass candlesticks but he let his kid sister have them in exchange for grandfather's shares in Australia.

Was this Mate a nut case or was this Mate a nut case? He was talking and I forced myself to listen, but I was scared. Who wouldn't be? He continued. 'So when Gaynor said she was going to marry this bloke I paid for the wedding. I just sold some cedar wood trees at the east side of my land and that paid for everything. About a hundred and forty guests that became four hundred or more and the party lasted three days or something.' He scratched his head as he tried to recall the event. 'No, it was longer than three days but that didn't matter. I sold some cedar wood trees because there was a forest of them on land you couldn't see from the house, anyway. They were a few miles away.'

He was now mumbling to himself a bit and I wasn't catching a single thing he was saying.

I cleared my throat and coughed quietly to catch his attention. His eyes focussed on me so I knew he was listening. 'How much are you actually worth financially, if you don't mind me asking?'

He pursed his lips and gazed at the deck head for a moment. 'Well, I bought the farm, had a new house built on it, bought the hens, pigs, cows and other things, like the lorries that run from my land to London with my eggs and I employ over sixty workers on the land and eight in the house. Well, that knocked a hole in my capital even if I did get rid of the pigs. Couldn't stand the smell.'

'How much capital do you actually have in the bank?'

'My accountants keep me informed. I have my own office of accountants and another with two solicitors. They tell me I have just over fourteen million, eight hundred and twenty-two thousand pounds.'

'Fourteen million p-p-pounds?' My voice squeaked.

'Yes. The two government officials that were here for my signature on the papers informed me of my latest figures. I agreed to spread all my hens' eggs on some of my fields so that Poland could afford to buy two navy destroyers in Newcastle.'

'Fourteen million pounds in the bank and ...?'

He pursed his lips and raised his head haughtily as if I had doubted him. 'The two government officials you met were instructed by my accountants to inform me that my capital stood at fourteen million, eight hundred and twenty two thousand pounds, seven hundred and fourteen pounds and eighteen pence.'

I was stunned. I rose to my feet still holding my beer and let my wobbly knees carry me to his cabin door.

'Oh, Second Engineer, you didn't pay me for that beer. You owe me twenty-five pence. Do you want a receipt for the money?'

A new Mate joined us when we arrived in Havana and our multi-millionaire Mate was escorted ashore by some sturdy men in white

coats and Poland didn't have two destroyers
built on the Tyne.

GUADELOUPE

In Yokohama I bought a pair of very high powered binoculars. They were the centre piece of an upmarket shop's display and accordingly very expensive but how many times in one's lifetime does one buy a pair of binoculars?

In our smoke room on board ship our Sparky had much to say about my purchase. 'You're daft!' he exploded. 'If you are looking at a ship on the horizon, you'll never hold them steady enough to see it.'

I sighed. 'Sparky, in the highlands of Scotland......'

'Any ship, even those in the highlands of Scotland. It doesn't matter what kind of ship you are on, you'll never get anything in focus. It stands to reason!'

Sparky was one of those rare individuals who had no problems with his hearing, but he had great difficulty in listening.

'I'll be using them in the Cairngorms......'

'It doesn't matter what company you're in, I still say you were daft to buy them.'

There were those amongst us who were convinced our Sparks should have gone on leave, stayed on leave, been left behind somewhere or quietly dropped overboard at sea on a dark night.

But Sparkies are a race apart from other seafarers. I, and many others, will always remember one called 'Bobo,'

Bobo, (few of us ever learned his real name,) could hold a sensible conversation with you, send out or receive messages in Morse and read a paperback book at the same time.

He had a huge Grundig radio in his cabin. It seems that during a spell on the Continent he spent some time in shops, examining all makes of powerful radios until he found what he was looking for, but he didn't buy it. Instead he sent an explanatory letter with some sketches and figures to show how their hipowered marine radio could be considerably improved. With a month, two of Grundig's hierarchy came on board our good ship and presented him with a new top quality Grundig marine radio, installed with his improvements, direct from the manufacturers, with their complements.

In the Far East, Bobo's radio reception of AFRTS and AFN was sweet and clear where our radios whistled and crackled and you didn't know if you were listening to the world news or the Bob Hope Show.

But our Sparky on our ship was no Bobo.

We sailed from Japan, flat out at nearly seven knots, heading for Guadeloupe in the Leeward Islands in the Caribbean to arrive many weeks later and anchored offshore near one of the islands to await orders.

The sun blazed down on us mercilessly and Captain Bill Bazill, Chief Engineer Bill

Higgins, the Mate Bill Court, the Second Mate Brian St John Early, the Sparky and I sat in the shade of the starboard outside alleyway. We were enjoying cold Japanese Kirin beers and they were discussing world affairs and how they could be put right.

I was sitting quietly with my binoculars focussed firmly on the far distant beach.

After they had come to their final conclusions on world affairs and how they should be put right, the Chief turned to look at me.

'Hey, Bob, are you OK? You haven't said a word in the last ten minutes.'

'Aye, Chief.'

The Captain had to have his say. 'Are you alright? What are you looking at? There's nothing out there on the horizon.'

I answered softly. 'Believe me or believe me not, gentlemen, but I am looking at a sandy beach full of beautiful girls in very tiny bikinis.'

They stared at me in silence. Suddenly, Chief Engineer Bill Higgins took the binoculars and looked for himself. The others held their breath.

'Come on, Chief, what do you see? Tell us, man.'

He blinked at each face in turn. 'There's a sandy beach over there, full of beautiful girls in tiny bikinis!'

Within minutes we had steam on deck, unleashed the starboard lifeboat, lowered it into the calm blue sea and headed for the sandy beach full of beautiful girls in tiny bikinis.

The Chief on lifeboat controls stopped the engine and allowed the lifeboat to cruise gently through the last fifty-plus yards to the beach. Because I had enough of the sun's blistering heat I jumped over the side and walked and the only part of me that was visible was my left hand holding one of the loops of rope that surround lifeboats.

I walked with the boat, gradually emerging from the water, until the boat beached and would go no further and I stood with the water lapping just below my knees.

I made a sweeping theatrical bow to our audience of wide-eyed beautiful girls in tiny bikinis. My action included their male escorts, too, of course.

They looked at me in amazement, so it seemed that the locals were friendly, especially when two handsome men jumped into the water, gripped me firmly and hurried me up on to the dry sand. I was flattered to find myself to be the centre of attraction.

A fair-haired gentleman, oozing with politeness, moved forward spoke in a strange language to my two escorts before turning to me.

'I can assume, sir, that you do not know this bay? You are unfamiliar with this area of the Caribbean?'

I was puzzled. Why were those two men so eager to get me out of the water? 'Nope, none of us have been here before.'

He nodded. 'Indeed, I would say that would account for it then.'

There were people moving closer and pointing at me in total amazement.

'Account for what?'

He cleared his throat, apologetically. 'You see, sir, this bay is the most natural breeding ground for great whites. It is the most densely populated shark bay in the whole Caribbean. To see you totally immersed in the water alarmed us, we didn't expect to see you reach the shore. We didn't expect to see you ever again. Indeed, sir, local people have been attacked by the sharks when standing ankle deep in the water.'

I was only vaguely aware that he was still talking but I never heard another word he said. I once had a bad encounter in Indonesia in 1962 in a flimsy dug out canoe and a big nasty shark and the thought of being carted off in a big hungry shark's mouth to depths unknown still terrifies me. I had nightmares about that for months.

We left the beach with the crowd watching Bill Bazill and Bill Court supporting me. I still had my teeth clenched and my body was shaking uncontrollably while the crowd stared. I had to fight this hysteria that was governing my body movements.

We entered the first public bar we came to, made our way to a table and Bill Court produced a very large whisky for me within seconds.

'Get it down you, wee Bob, and I'll get you another.'

During this time I was thinking how ridiculous I must look, behaving like a five-year old boy that had just seen a ghost.

Before Bill could return with my second large whisky a smartly dressed young man approached our table.

'I am informed that you were the gentleman who waded in our bay. Do you mind?' While he was speaking he politely held my wrist and stared at his watch.

'Your pulse is bloody high, dear fellow, bloody high, if you will excuse my French.' He turned to Bill Bazill. 'Would I be correct in assuming you are the Captain of the vessel in the bay? You are? Good. I am a doctor, Ivan Igor Sladovski and I think I should take your friend...'

'Bob, he's called 'Bob,' Sparky burst out.

'.....your friend Bob home with me. At home I can inject him with tranquilisers and other medications as necessary. It is essential he sleeps soundly through the night. What if I suggest we meet you here on the beach then at, say, ten o'clock tomorrow morning?'

So it was agreed.

The Doctor and his companion, their two lovely young wives and I travelled in a three-litre Chrysler to a large super bungalow of a type that is only ever seen in Hollywood movies. The front of this bungalow had a veranda with two tables, six chairs and two servants, poised and eager to please. I was also very aware of the two ladies in their flimsy cotton dresses but they were my hosts and, with an effort, I behaved as a guest should in those circumstances. I was very much indebted to them. But it had been a very long, lonely journey from Yokohama....

'You are not English, Bob?'

'No, I am Scottish.'

'Ah! Scottish! Tell us about your Scottish land.'

Just at that moment Doctor Sladovski appeared with a small tray containing a few medical items and he inoculated me.

'I'll give you another before we retire for the night, Bob. But tell us about your country, your Scottish land.'

With Bill Court's two large whiskies below my belt and the good doctor's inoculation in my arm, my condition was improving steadily so I told them all I could think of about my Scotland.

The evening wore on, the sun's blistering heat had reduced to a pleasant warmth and I was no longer trembling like a leaf in a gale force wind.

I am sure the young doctor's name was Sladovski but the names of the others I have long since forgotten. He told me that their predecessors had fled from Russia when communism ravaged their land. Guadeloupe was just one of the hiding places that were unlikely to be disturbed by Communism due to its close proximity to America.

The doctor injected me once more, making a total of three injections then his lovely young wife took my hand and led me to a beautiful bedroom with an adjoining bathroom. She opened a drawer and placed a set of white pyjamas on the bed.

'They might just fit you, Bob. Now leave your clothes outside the door and the servants will wash them and press them for you, ready for the morning.'

As she was leaving she smiled and blew me a kiss.

I showered and found my agony was beginning again in spite of the medication I had received. I bit my lips, clenched my teeth and tried to stop shaking.

I was still trembling when I went to bed and visions of sharks were still in my mind ready to attack every time I shut my eyes.

The door opened, the Doctor's young wife came and slipped into bed with me, cradled me in her arms and kissed me.

'Hey! What if your husband.......'

'Don't be silly, my darling Bob,' she breathed in my ear. 'He told me I must go to your bed and comfort you. He says it is essential.'

But to return to Bobo's Super Grundig Radio, I did better. At home I bought a neat little radio cassette player, recorded all the good plays and stories and returned to sea with about forty radio programmes I could listen to when it pleased me.

And it doesn't take up too much room in my luggage either.

BEHIND FAULTS

When I served my five years apprenticeship in one of the mightiest heavy engine workshops on the Clyde I learned many things from my ageing workmates and not all were about engines.

When the subject of haemorrhoids came up, many could tell you tales that reduced Frankenstein and Dracula horror stories into comic book tales by comparison. One of my elderly afflicted work mates told me stories of being in hospital and made to kneel in a bath because every time his bowels moved his stitches tore off and his back passage had to be re-stitched. It became a daily occurrence over many weeks.

One elderly Chief Engineer couldn't even stand after his operation and had to be lifted on to his ship by a cargo winch. His operation forced him to live lying face down in his bunk on a plastic sheet and an Indian steward most grudgingly fed him his meals that way. The Chief Steward, not being Indian, had volunteered to attend to all matters at the other end. It was a week before they could find a replacement for their patient.

I was in my early forties when fate decided I had been too fortunate too long and decreed I should suffer the same fate as many of my engineering compatriots and I was inflicted with piles.

I chose to be operated on in the Merchant Navy Hospital in London, with professionals who were highly experienced in these matters and this was arranged in a matter of hours from our own surgery in Scarborough. Next day my dear wife and I set off by train and taxi to the great throbbing metropolis of London.

We found the hospital to be a long wide hallway with doors on one side and rows of benches as one might expect to find in an airport waiting room. There were medical staff and equipment everywhere and everything was meticulously clean and polished.

'Mr Jackman? Come with me please.'

She was a fifty-ish nursing assistant with a pleasant smile and she led me to one of the long row of doors and into a room where everything was painted brilliant white. A broad shelf protruded from the wall.

'Please undress from the waist down, Mr Jackman, and lie on the shelf, thank you.'

When I had done so, she carefully washed my rear end with a sponge and a liquid that smelled like methylated spirits and probably was methylated spirits. But I could be wrong.

'There now, you can sit up again.' She was all smiles.

The moment I feared was approaching.

During my years at sea, on three separate occasions I have had to pull out a tooth with a pair of engine room pliers. This is often met with total disbelief from those who live on land, a mere mile or less from anaesthetics and qualified dentists. But no ship's Captain is going to alter course to the nearest port because one crew member has toothache.

Furthermore, that crew member is unlikely to be excused duties because he has toothache.

When the situation demands it, you can cope with pain and I was tensing myself for the ordeal I was about to endure on that shelf.

The nursing assistant was drying her hands when the door opened and a surgeon and a girl entered, both dressed from necks to ankles in white gowns.

'Ah, Mr Robert Jackman? Yes. I hope you do not object to my assistant being with us? She is enthusiastic in this particular field of surgery.'

She was young and beautiful and though I have often met many beautiful girls in my forty-plus years, I generally had my trousers on when I did so. Well, during my first meeting with them anyway.

Again, experience in life taught me a lot. I found that when I get into a tough situation where I need to bear pain, I can survive better with a touch of humour.

'Well, Doctor, I don't think it is quite proper for this very young lady to be allowed to perform an operation on my private parts when we have not even been introduced.'

So there were introductions and smiles all round then I was positioned with my back to them and my rear end overhanging the edge of the shelf.

The operation began.

I listened to the surgeon explaining to the girl what he was doing and why he was doing it. How they both could see so much internally amazed me, and I heard every word: I shall place the loop high above the lower haemorrhoid and the nerve then tighten it firmly...... Now I can cut both of them free like so..... Now I want you to do the same..... Keep the loop well above the nerve. Higher... That's perfect...... Now close the loop, tighten and cut........ Steady..... Yes, Miss Shepherd, you did that perfectly. A perfect job, well done.

They were finished. It was all over.

'Lie still until you can sit up now, Mr Jackman, and Miss Shepherd will stay with you for a few moments longer. And, nurse, when Mr Jackman feels steady enough to stand upright, you will see him out to the waiting room.' He turned to his beautiful assistant. 'You did a good job. I couldn't have done it any better myself.' Smiles all round, and then he turned and left.

It was a few minutes before I was allowed off the shelf to stand upright and my legs were trembling. There was no blood, no pain and I could feel my legs steadying as the moments passed. Both ladies helped to dress me.

The nursing assistant and the beautiful young student doctor stood on either side of me, and then the nursing assistant, such an understanding lady, moved away a little. After a moment the young student doctor, moved away too.

Though my legs were wobbly, I fought to remain upright with them standing ready to catch me. But I was in no pain. **I was in no pain!**

For the sake of something to say, I blurted, 'Why does a lovely creature like you specialise in operations like the one you just put me through? Why specialise in haemorrhoids?'

We were now facing each other and she straightened my shirt collar before looking at me.

'When I was a child I loved my grandparents very much. Grandad, however was often in pain and had problems when he went to the toilet. These were things that I was too young to understand, things that couldn't be mentioned in front of a child. He had many years of agony and medical treatments that didn't help him much. As the years went on, I gathered bits of information on what his problem was and the horror of all he and Granny had been through over the long years. I learned that in the beginning he had been forced to stay kneeling in a bath because every time his bowels moved his stitches tore off and had to be replaced. His treatments lasted for weeks. Agonising weeks.'

We stood silently facing each other, and then I took both her hands and warmly kissed the palm in each. My feelings were far beyond words and she knew that.

I had no discomfort in the taxis or the trains back to Scarborough. Now I am in my eighties and my backside still works beautifully, thanks to a beautiful young student doctor and her long-suffering Grandfather.

Then the thought came to me. Her name was 'Shepherd', her grandfather had suffered all the agonies of haemorrhoids and the agonies of stitches coming out every time his bowels moved. That was why she specialised in the surgery of haemorrhoids and it was now surgery without pain.

I worked with an old Bob Shepherd in the Heavy Engine Works on the Clyde who told me of the agonies and the humiliation he had suffered with piles over many years.

I wonder if she was his granddaughter. She might have been.

LI YANG

Li Yang was our impeccable Chinese Chief Steward, a steward and master chef who could have successfully commanded any of the top five-star restaurants or hotels in any of the world's greatest civilised cities. He ran our ship's catering department with extreme efficiency and his staff were proud to have a man of his calibre as their leader.

He was aloof and groomed immaculately to oversee all culinary details at meal times and should any courses be returned to the kitchen unfinished, he noticed and investigated. He was proud of his command of English, and used it in correctly typing the menus. He had a selection of English, French and Chinese cookery books to assist him. He never at any time asked assistance with the names of dishes or the writing of menus. Consequently, mistakes in his department were rare and the service was without equal on any ship we had ever been on before.

Leaving Yokohama we sailed to Australia to pick up a cargo and were obliged to wait for a few days somewhere in the remote west coast, many miles away from nowhere. Inland was one enormous empty desert and the little port where we docked was no more than a dozen houses, barely half of which were occupied.

At 'Finished With Engines', boiler suits were off, we showered, pre-lunch beers were out, and feet were resting lightly on the smoke room tables when a spitting image of Rolf Harris entered.

'Hi, fellows. My name's Don.' He spent a few minutes shaking our hands. 'Great. You wanna go on a kangaroo shoot? I supply the transport, the evening meal, shoot as many roos as you want and you can bring back some kangaroo parts for the kitchen. I pick you up at four o'clock this afternoon; get you back eight o'clock tomorrow morning if you are lucky. I charge you twenty quid a head, no charge at all if you don't get at least one kangaroo. What do you say?'

This was certainly very different from 'girly bars', cinemas, or the wild life of some ports we could mention. Again, it was a pleasure to get off the ship for a while and see a vast area of dry land as opposed to the terrific emptiness of the Pacific Ocean. It was something new so he had four customers before we finished our beers.

At the appointed hour of four o'clock, ever-attentive Li Yang had a box made up containing a selection of sandwiches, cartons of fruit juice, paper cups and, with a large case of our own beer, we were ready to shoot any kangaroos that showed their faces in West Australia.

Bob Pocock was the Mate, Ronnie Phelan was Junior Second Engineer, I was Second Engineer and we had a Chief Engineer who shall remain nameless. Bob and I were very wary of giving Ronnie a gun when the afore-mentioned Chief Engineer who shall remain nameless, was within shooting distance.

My curiosity overcame me. 'Chief, why did you want to come along on this kangaroo shoot?' He examined his fingers before replying. 'The Captain ordered it. He paid my twenty quid. He said it would do me good to get off the ship for a while,' he smirked.

That could be taken two ways. Captain Charles Lorrimer, a gentleman of the highest order who was liked by all, was probably hoping the Chief would be lost in the desert or shot in the head.

Our Chief who shall remain nameless was pleased to inform all of us how he met the Owner, the Captain and the Chief Mate of a beautiful cargo ship tied up near us in Yokohama and they had a wonderful, expensive time together.

We all remember every word when our Chief proudly told the story. 'I organised it that the Owner footed the bill for everything on the first night. The second night, Tuesday, their Captain paid for everything and it cost him plenty. The Chief Mate footed the bill for everything on Wednesday night, tons of cash changed hands and it was my turn to pay on Thursday night.' He smirked, his fat little body twitching in pleasure as he looked at each of our faces. 'I knew we were sailing on Thursday morning. That's why I said I would pay on Thursday. Now that's what I call being smart.'

That was just one of his stories we had in mind when we left the port in Western Australia and sped into one of the flattest of all the world's flat lands. There was not a mark on that flatness, not a stone, not a buttercup, and we now sped along for about four hours in absolute nothingness.

'We'll be in Suzanville pretty soon, guys, and they'll sure have a dinner waiting for us. By the way, Bob, you are a burgoo walloper?'

That made me think. 'I don't know about being what you called 'a burgoo walloper'. I like to think of myself as a two-fisted pacifist.'

We were doing about sixty miles an hour when he swivelled round in the driving seat. 'Burgoo is what they call porridge in these parts, and a burgoo walloper is a guy who eats porridge. A Scotchman is a burgoo walloper.'

'But we hope you are not hinting that our dinner in this Suzanville is going to be porridge or burgoo,' I smiled.

So we arrived in Suzanville: Eight wooden lean-to houses, one shop, a doss house of sorts and a combined hotel, restaurant and pub. They seated us in the public bar-cum-restaurant-cum-games-room at a long wooden table, a bottle of Melbourne Victoria Bitter to mark each place and a large soup plate in front of each of us. A big tray of freshly baked crisp bread rolls came next, then the woman in charge came, carrying a large basin of stew with vegetables.

Her ladle scooped large servings on to all our plates, then she placed the basin on the table.

'Eat up, you fellows, and there's plenty more if you want it.'

She then stood with her hands on her broad hips at my end of the table to ensure we were satisfied with the meal.

I smiled up at her. 'Tell me, dear lady, have you always lived out here in the desert?'

'Hell, no, Blue! I've lived right here in the middle of this town all my life.'

The meal was good, they were friendly and when we got up to leave, all the locals drinking at the bar left their glasses, came over and they all shook hands with the four of us to wish us well.

So, back into the Land Rover we again made our way at break neck speed in the dark, further into the dead flat desert but now with our headlamps on full beam. Don had a spotlight fitted on the roof of the Land Rover that he could swivel in wide arcs, scanning the darkness ahead of us.

Suddenly, about three hours later, there was a pack of kangaroos in the distance, caught up in our beams of light.

'Let's go get them, guys. Wahoo!'

So we roared after them at speed, all lights in full beam and succeeded in pumping bullets into quite a few of them. Then we turned and went back to tally up.

There were five dead and two badly wounded. Don had a machete, a sort of short heavy sword, and he cut the throats of the two wounded ones.

'I use this to finish them off,' he explained. 'Bullets cost money and I won't leave them suffering.'

He continued to hack away at one of the kangaroos and finished the task by putting its two haunches in new Hessian bags and stowing them on the roof of the Land Rover.

While he was doing this, I opened Li Yang's box and held it out for the others to help themselves to the sandwiches. The Chief who shall remain nameless, took a sandwich, opened it to examine it, shook his head then dropped it on top of the others. He was repeating the performance with another sandwich when I swivelled the box away from him.

'Hey! I haven't got one yet.' He snarled angrily with his lower lip jutted out.

'We got them to eat. We didn't get them for you to play with.' From the box I removed the sandwich he had unwrapped and pushed it into his hands.

'I don't want the bliddy thing now that you have handled it,' he stormed.

'Well, we don't want the bliddy thing now that you have handled it.'

He went quiet and sulked. 'But that's different.'

By this time Don had done his butchering and came to join us.

'Give us a hand with the sandwiches, Don.'

This time it was Ronny, our Irish Junior Second who made the offer and was holding out the box.

'Right, blue, sure will, good on ya.' Don took one from the box.

'THESE ARE OUR SANDWICHES!!' The Chief screamed. 'THEY ARE NOT HIS SANDWICHES!! IF HE WANTED SANDWICHES HE SHOULD HAVE BROUGHT HIS OWN.'

We do get nasty types at sea sometimes and Ronny's face was white with rage when I grabbed him and took him and Bob Pocock to one side. I called loud enough for my voice to carry back to the Chief.

'Hey, Don, how far are we from the nearest town?'

'The one we came through? Suzanville? Well, I reckon it's a full hundred and thirty miles but you could easily miss it in the dark.'

'Thanks, Don, one hundred and thirty miles to that wee town called Suzanville?' Again I shouted it so the Chief could hear.

This was one way of informing the Chief that he was on very thin ice in a very big desert, where he could easily get lost in the dark. He quietened considerably. In fact, he remained quiet all the way back to the ship and was very relieved when we finally arrived on board. But, of course, once he was safely on board the good ship he returned to being his usual repulsive self.

Li Yang and his staff was delighted with the two kangaroo haunches, even more so when

Bob, Ronny and I insisted that both haunches were to be divided equally among everyone on board. We had six European and thirty-one Chinese and if we had made it one haunch to us and one haunch to them, we Europeans would have been eating kangaroo stew three times a day for a month.

Our Chief was highly indignant. 'Why should we let the crew have one of the haunches? They didn't pay anything. We paid good money to go out all night and shoot kangaroos, not them.'

When we were more than ready for our first kangaroo joint dinner, Li Yang informed us: 'Only when kangaroo meat is rested.'

But a week went passed. We knew the crew had sung its praises many times, but we hadn't had a taste of roasted kangaroo and we were getting impatient. By chance, on the following Sunday I went into the galley and found our whole haunch was sizzling beautifully on the galley stove and the smell made my teeth start sweating.

'Ah! Chief Cook, this one dinner today?'

'May be. Li Yang ploblem liting meh nu.'

Translated, he was telling me that the meticulous Li Yang had had a problem writing the menu. No cooking problem, just a writing problem. Everything was delayed because the menu had to be right. He had spent a few troubled days studying his Chinese/English dictionaries. When the menu did arrive on the

officers' saloon table, he had finally entered the main course as 'Self-Hunting Kangaroo.'
And it was delicious!

A MATTER OF TASTE

My reputation as a judoka began one evening in a quiet little port somewhere in Malaysia. A town of narrow streets, paraffin lamps and the only traffic in the narrow streets was an occasional three-wheel rickshaw or bicycle. Unusual items on display on one of the native stalls had caught my attention and I had stopped to look at them when suddenly a pair of strong arms grabbed me from behind.

My assailant towered over me so his centre of gravity was almost level with my shoulders so I flipped my unknown assailant over my right shoulder and he landed slap-bang on the pavement, thereby hurting both his bum and his dignity.

He happened to be the big burly Sparky from the ship, failing in his attempt to be funny. His two companions witnessing the event that day were our deck cadets, so in order to preserve some standing with the others on board our ship, he broadcast far and wide that he heard I was a master class black belt judo expert. He emphasised it was obvious that only a master class black belt judo expert could have thrown a big chap like him. Had the truth be known, my talents in Judo, Ju-Jitsu and Karate began and ended as a ten-tear-old with other ten-year-olds in the school playground nearly forty years earlier.

On other ships in the company, the more I denied having such a mighty talent, the more fellow seafarers believed otherwise and wonderful imaginative tales of my prowess grew. They thought I was being modest but though I am a creature with a fair share of faults, modesty is not one of them.

Many months later I joined the good ship MV Inchstaffa and within minutes the cheery lads on board were in the Chief's cabin with the beers out helping us to become acquainted. We were all starting into our second bottle of Asahi when the dinner gong rang and they gulped down what remained of their contents then hurried to the dining saloon.

'The Captain gets nasty if any of us are late for meals,' Chief Engineer Bill Halewood whispered as we scampered out of his cabin.

So I clambered into my uniform and made my way to the dining saloon. Here I found the seating arrangement was very different from anything I had ever seen on similar ships.

As normal practice in these ships that only carried six British officers, the Captain's place was set at the head of the table with the Chief Engineer on his right and the Mate on his left. But our Chief Engineer was seated rather inconspicuously down two spaces from him and my place was at the bottom end, facing up the table to the Captain's empty chair. Everyone spoke in whispers waiting to being served.

Eventually the man himself made an entrance and we had total silence. The steward waited until the Captain was seated, handed him the menu and then served him. We all waited silently and patiently until eventually it was our turn to be served.

After a few mouthfuls he pushed his plate back, put his elbows on the table, rested his chin on his hands and stared at me hard for a while before speaking. Most Captains would say something pleasant to welcome a new officer on board but this character was different.

He said quietly. 'So you're the Judo champion of the company?'

The piece of fish on my fork stopped halfway to my mouth and I looked at him for a few moments before I put it in my mouth.

He raised his voice. 'Answer when I speak to you!'

I hate bullies. Even as a child in school I would put my fists up to defend anyone, including myself, being bullied and now in my forties that feeling still ranked a long way above many others. Having given and received a few bloodied noses in my time has never changed me.

I smiled. 'What was it you wanted to know?'

The silence crackled like static electricity and the others kept their eyes fixed on their plates.

He threw his serviette down on the table and stood up. 'I'll talk to you later, Jackman.'

Merchant Navy – What A Life

'It's Mister Jackman,' I called after him quite pleasantly as he stormed out of the saloon. Probably that's why we never became friends. I wondered what kind of shipping companies he had sailed in before? Most Captains I had sailed with were pleasant, highly competent in their jobs and had no qualms about sailing 'behind God's back' in battered old ships like the 'Inchstaffa'. They were the kind of men who had made the British Merchant Navy the finest Merchant Navy in the world. This aggressive twit was an exception.

A week passed and the Chief and I were having a beer or two together in his cabin when the Captain walked in. He didn't knock; he just opened the door, walked in, planted himself on the settee facing me and ignored the Chief.

'If you are an expert in judo, where did you learn it?'

'Good evening, Captain.'

He paused before answering. 'Remember who you are talking to. Now where did you learn this judo thing?'

'It's a long story. Are you sure you want to hear it?'

He got up, went to the Chief's refrigerator, helped himself to one of the Chief's beers without a word and sat down again facing the two of us.

'Go on then.'

'The name 'Jackman' doesn't mean anything to you, does it?'

He shook his head.

I swilled the beer around in my bottle for a moment and took a deep breath. 'It began in the Great War. British troops were being shown a new way to do a bayonet attack. They were taught to put their left hand on top of their rifle. The idea was to lunge with the bayonet, slash down with the rifle, then hit the German an uppercut with the butt. It was my father's brother that showed the British experts that the Germans could easily knock the rifle and bayonet down out of the soldier's hands as he lunged. It was a Captain Royston MacGregor of the Queen's Own Cameron Highlanders that backed my uncle's story and so Scottish soldiers stuck to the old way of using the bayonet and their bayonet charges were much more successful.'

'Ok. What's that got to do with you learning judo?' He snorted disdainfully.

'My Uncle Bob survived the war and stayed with the army. He was invited to study more about hand-to-hand combat and learned that the Japanese were experts at it. They had their own style of attacking someone with little danger to themselves, even if the other fellow was holding a knife or a club. My uncle stayed with the army and the army granted him something called a 'good will posting' to Osaka in Japan to learn their ways of defence and attack. He became a master of all grades of Judo, Jiu-Jitsu and Karate. In those days, he was the only European to be taught these arts because the Japanese held them as sacred as other countries hold their religion. They are handed down from father to son over many generations.'

I took another mouthful of beer before continuing with my fairy story.

'Well, go on.' The Captain insisted, scowling, but unsure of himself. 'Don't bliddy well stop there.'

I smiled and made him wait, then went on: 'My Uncle Bob was in South Africa in 1940 when he learned that he had a nephew named after him. He had never married but he was never without a woman when he wanted one. Finally, when he learned about me, he gave up the army and everything connected with it and came back to the UK. I was his only nephew, I was ten years old and my lessons in unarmed combat started then.'

It was obvious that neither the Captain nor the Chief were going to believe me. I shook my head as if I was bored with it all.

'Aw! For Heaven's sake!' It was pure fiction and I had to make it convincing, but my 'facts' had come from a comic book I read somewhere. 'Captain, hold out your right hand as if I was going to put something in it. That's right. Now tense the muscles. Tense all the muscles from the tip of the middle finger to the point of the elbow. OK? Tighter. Now, close the fingers together and place the thumb in your palm. Keep the muscles hard.'

I watched him clench his teeth as he persevered with my instructions. Finally he gasped and let his whole arm go slack.

'Do it ten times ten in the morning, Captain, and ten times ten in the evening for a month. I don't mean for a couple of days, I mean for a month. When your whole forearm becomes as hard as cast iron you can ram it into a man's stomach, grab his bottom rib and break it. You can even pull it out of his stomach if you lash out with the sole of your foot against his goolies. But that's being nasty and it's not fair.'

I finished my beer, dropped the empty into the Chief's waste basket and turned to leave.

'Goodnight, Chief. Don't let him drink all your beer.'

My lesson to the Captain was pure fabrication, beautiful five star fiction from a book I had read somewhere in my teenage days, but he believed me. Maybe it was the way I told it. Maybe I'm getting good at spinning yarns?

Weeks went by, our cargo discharged in Japan and a bulletin from the company headquarters informed us that our next port to load was quite undecided at that time and we were ordered to sail south until further orders.

Then it came to pass that our next port was Djakarta in Indonesia and we would take a local agent on board to organise the labour and supervise all cargo work.

We found there were three rates of exchange in the currency offered in those far off days. The first was the Government rate which meant a bottle of local beer cost more than £3.00. The tourist rate meant a bottle of local beer cost about 80p. Then there was the Black Market Rate, a rate that the Indonesian people offered that dropped the price of a bottle of beer to a mere 20p if bought with a European currency: any European currency. Every town and mud hut village was desperately crying out for foreign currencies.

Our Captain, being the bully he was, insisted on all financial dealings being at the Government rate so our stock of Japanese beer and other delights went down rather quickly. Ship's water in tropical climes has little to recommend it.

It also meant that buying food for the ship was more than double or triple what it could have been and consequently the chandlers ashore supplied us with the poorest quality imaginable. Food was plentiful ashore, but selling their food for worthless rupiahs infuriated them. If paid in foreign currencies they could be very generous. So we went quite hungry and slightly thirsty to the delight of our sadistic Captain.

Our crew were Hong Kong Chinese and they, like us, loved the Captain not at all.

But they (bless 'em) met with Chinese chandlers on shore and they had some long talks together. Our Chinese crew had their families in Hong Kong transfer Hong Kong dollars into other banks in Hong Kong in the names of the Indonesian Ship Chandlers. The chandlers, in turn, paid all our Chinese crew in great fistfuls of Indonesian rupiahs.

As a bonus and to show their pleasure, the delighted chandlers had a big fat pig barbequed and delivered to the ship in the ship's lifeboat. It was so tenderly cooked that pieces were sagging and breaking off and the pig was still sizzling hot when it arrived. All the sweet and sour accompaniments were there, with char sui trimmings, black bean sauce, rare vegetables, assorted peppers and other delicacies too numerous to mention.

We were warmly invited to the aft deck by our crew, with the exception of the Captain, who was not informed.

It was carefully hauled on board at the crew's end and our catering department dashed around handing us plates, bowls, cutlery and chopsticks. We served ourselves sweet, delicious lumps of pork and vegetables, pork so tender you could lift chunks off with your chopsticks and vegetables so exotic we ate every tiny scrap. We gorged ourselves on our first decent meal in many weeks.

The crew also produced Japanese Asahi and Kirin beers and pressed them upon the Chief, the Mate, Second Mate, the Sparks and me.

Suddenly the Captain appeared, nonchalantly strolling down the deck and all went quiet. He didn't look at any of us sitting on the hatch; he looked at our plates and then at the big delicious barbequed pig.

He barked: 'Chief Steward!'

Ma Lang, the Chief Steward, went and stood in front of him with his hands clasped and his head bowed. 'Yes, Captain?'

'Take a plateful of that pig up to my cabin, and put plenty of the trimmings with it,' he scowled. Then he strolled back down the deck again to the midship accommodation.

We all watched him go. The Chief Steward sighed, picked up a used unwashed plate and started to put pieces of the pork on it.

'I'll do that, Chief Steward,' I smiled. When he and I looked at each other he knew I was up to something so, with barely a moment's hesitation, he let me have the plate. In fact, he almost smiled.

'Ah, so. Velly good.'

I put a variety of pork pieces with the sweet and sour sauce, the black bean sauce, the exotic vegetables and strips of crispy skin on to the plate. Then I handed it to him. He bowed to me, and he tried not to smile as he made his way to the Captain's cabin.

Returning to sit with the Chief and the others, I knew the crew were wondering about me filling the Captain's plate and Ma Lang saying nothing.

Twenty minutes later we were sitting on the after hatch when Ma Lang returned, carrying the empty plate. He stopped before me.

'Everything okay, Chief Steward?'

'Captain speak all velly good. Captain speak, pork stuffing velly much strange thing but good.' His face broke into a huge smile then he began giggling so much his whole body was shaking. 'He eat it all up.'

We looked at each other for a moment longer then he hurried to tell the crew. Suddenly there was a terrific roar of laughter and cheering from all of them. They looked at me and waved.

The Chief turned to me. 'What in the Hell is happening, Bob? You very carefully filled the Captain's plate with all the choice bits you could find. Are you giving in to the man? Why didn't the Chief Steward fill his plate? Why you? And how come our beloved Captain got pork stuffing and none of us got any of this pork stuffing? What's happening? And where did all the pork stuffing come from, Bob?'

I turned to the Chief and the others. 'The pork stuffing I gave to the Captain? I scooped it out of the pig's back passage, Chief.'

THE BOOKS

Our Chinese shipping company bought her from Chinese owners and re-named her the 'MV Inchmull'. She was lying at anchor in Hong Kong when all six of us joined in one afternoon and found her officers and crew had already left without a 'hello', 'good-bye' or 'kiss my ass Kilmarnock.' Our Chinese officers and crew had taken over and one of the saloon tables had been pressed into service by shoreside bureaucratic nonentities employed in 'signing us on articles.' The new Chinese catering department were in overdrive checking the food supplies and coping with lunch for us, the new arrivals. Eventually articles were signed and some order was restored.

As Second Engineer I had had a quick check in the engine room to ensure all was well and found my new Chinese Third Engineer already in charge with two donkeymen on watch. He and I had a look round together to ensure everything was warming through, ready for 'stand by'.

Up top, there was the usual hustle and bustle of unpacking suitcases, finding uniform gear, introducing one's self to the others and shaking hands.

All good fun blended with an erratic mixture of panic and perplexity but eventually we did 'sign on articles', we did have lunch and we did finally sail for Chingwantao in North China that evening. As in many instances like this, many surprises came to light, one being the fact that there was nothing written in English anywhere on board. Not a book, pamphlet or magazine of any kind except for one, a German pin-up magazine found wedged down the back of the Second Mate's bunk. However, since none of us could speak German and its previous owner had cut the pictures out, it was of little interest.

I do remember the bottle of brown sauce on our saloon table with a label in English. It read, 'H.W. Brand, past master in the art of cookery to His Majesty King George IV, delighted in making special sauces to tempt the royal palate. One day, however, he excelled himself. 'Brand,' exclaimed His Majesty. 'This sauce is A1'. And so it has remained to the present day, Brand's A1 Sauce.'

How exciting.

This was the only piece of writing in English on board other than what we had brought with us, which was, namely one 'Readers Digest', a book on crossword puzzles for beginners, and a brochure on Morris Minor motor cars.

Our trip began on the first days of the Chinese winter. Then, for five months we battered that old ship from Chingwantao, Dairen and Tsing-Tao up and down to Shanghai, with commando dockers ashore working day and night at reckless speed, loading and unloading our cargoes of coal. Winches that broke down had to be repaired and put in good working order before arriving in the next port and this often meant exhausted engineers and fitters working overnight at sea to repair them. In calm seas and mild weather it was tiring enough but because the winter months had set in, the ship had to crunch its way through sheet ice and we had layers of brittle snow covering everything on the winches and the deck. That was true hardship. Winches had to be in good working order for arrival in the next port and words I wrote in a poem years earlier kept coming to mind:

'Outside in the snow it was forty below,
And the wind screeched like banshees in Hell......'

The air temperature when we worked on deck was truly 'forty below'. Thermometers don't go any lower than that. We wore thick quilted coats, jackets, hats and gauntlets given freely by the Chinese authorities at the Mission in Chingwantao but we had to buy our own fur lined boots. Ashore, all Chinese men, woman and children were wrapped up in the same attire.

It was nearly impossible to put nuts on to bolts when you are wearing thick heavy gauntlets and if you take the gauntlets off, the freezing temperatures burned your fingers within a few minutes and stuck to them.

Eventually, the icy weather eased off and we even saw the sun again. Then the glorious news came that we were to return to every seaman's idea of Heaven, Hong Kong, for forty eight hours. A whole forty-eight hours of the bright lights, the beautiful girls, wining, dining and dancing – the sheer thought of it after the ice bound Hell we had been through for most of the last five months was exhilarating!

Bob Graham, one of the finest Chief Engineers I ever sailed with, informed me that our shipping company had arranged an engine room squad to give us a break by doing any maintenance work required. I had a work list about the size of the two Sunday Telegraphs with supplements. Our Sparky nearly broke his neck tumbling down the stairs from the bridge to give him the message and Captain Mel Hooper nodded his approval.

Paddy Keilly, our young second mate loved all women, madly and foolishly. That boy's loins were straining to be ashore in Hong Kong and his alcohol content needed replenishing too.

The First Mate, who shall remain nameless, was a forty-year-old bewildered soul whose father owned a car showroom in London that sold Bentley and Rolls Royce cars. We had a strong suspicion that he had persuaded his son to make a career for himself in the Merchant Navy, preferably in ships that stayed well away from the United Kingdom in general and London in particular.

He was jumping with joy at the news. 'I say, how wonderful, chaps! We shall be able to buy books! I, personally, shall buy lots and lots of lovely books!'

At that point we slipped up. Books were the last thing on our minds when the anchor went down in Hong Kong. We read our mail from home, got dressed 'for the beach' but shopping for books still dominated our Mate's tiny mind. The remaining five of us contributed generously towards his intended shopping spree round the bookshops.

Then there was our mad twenty-four hours ashore savouring the delights of everything that Hong Kong had to offer. Finally we felt relaxed and at peace with the world, enough to return to the old Inchmull and force her and us back to the horrors of the North China Coast.

This time, we consoled ourselves; we knew we now had a large assortment of books in English, as chosen by our Mate. But our Mate's choice consisted of leather-bound volumes of an 'Encyclopaedia of Animals Found in Upper Yukon,' 'Verses by Greek Apostles before Cato', 'Life in Central Ghana with President Gio Tawla', 'Lesser Known Tributaries of the River Marjata' and others of a similar nature.

We did not appreciate his selection and I have a suspicion some of the younger ones, myself included, nearly shed tears in exasperation. Furthermore, it confirmed our thoughts on why our Mate was not living a comfortable life at home in London with his father, selling Bentley and Rolls Royce cars to the aristocracy.

At sea, books are essential. If you are not on watch, you are catching up on some sleep. If you are not catching up on sleep you have missed, you are sitting in your cabin staring at the bulkhead waiting for the days to go past. That's why books are so important. Mentally they take your mind off the ship for a while, to interesting places with heroes and lovely wenches doing daring things but there was nothing like that in the books the Mate had chosen. Nothing!

In desperation, I began writing stories about that time and the others quite liked them. Again, they would probably have liked anything any idiot had written by this time, providing it was in English. My stories were written with ball point pens on airmail writing pads, but they were read by all.

Five long exhausting months passed and again we returned to Hong Kong. This time, those of us who depended on the English language for communicating with our fellow men, went ashore and bought great bundles of sensible paperbacks of our choice and returned to the ship before we even smiled at a dancing girl. Then after we said 'Hello' etc, etc, etc, to the fair young maidens, quenched our raging thirsts and had a dance or six, etc, etc, etc, we returned to our old ship in the morning, burdened with yet more books.

Merchant Navy – What A Life

Our Chinese carpenter, Ma Ling, made a beautiful job of erecting a grand array of shelves in the officers' smoke room and we filled the shelves from end to end, with paperback books.

Months went by and there were a few changes in officers and crew. We had a new Mate called 'Bill' and he had brought his wife on board. Bill was pear shaped, red-faced and breathless and he waddled like a ruptured duck. Helena was of very similar stature but she could talk endlessly without stopping for breath. Still, they were a pleasant couple to have on board, even though Bill was strictly forbidden by his Helena to partake of alcohol and her word was law in that and other subjects. With husband Bill, her word was law on all subjects.

Summer had come with a vengeance when we arrived in a port called Dairen, a coal port that China rented out to Japan and Russia at various times over the years. These outside powers had built a form of overhead railway system that looped-the-loop and made the trucks turn upside down at the highest point and unload their coal in a giant hopper. From there, it poured into our cargo holds. They probably copied the designs of those who built the scenic railway in Blackpool's Amusement Park.

But it had broken down! No cargo would be loaded for a few days! A few days!

There was sheer, heavenly pleasure in sitting or lying down on the wooden deck outside our accommodation, silently absorbing the sun's warmth and goodness, all six of us easing our tired muscles aided by the cooling influence of a case of Shanghai Export. I could feel tiredness oozing out of my weary muscles as I lay there. Others groaned in sheer bliss between mouthfuls of beer.

'Where's the wife, Bill?' I asked without opening my eyes.

Before answering, he reached for another bottle of beer in the carton where the beers were steadily decreasing in numbers.

'In the cabin,' he murmured. 'I think she is reading something.'

A few minutes' silence, then Bob Graham lazily murmured: 'Which book? We got hundreds.'

'I think it's called, 'NEXT PLEASE.' Or something like that.'

Sparky shot upright. 'What a book! It has sex-sex-sex on every page. Great chunks of sex! All in detail! I wondered where that book went! And there are lots of pictures too! Pictures of them doing it!'

We all silently made a mental note of the name of the book mentioned, looked at each other, but remained silent.

Suddenly Bill spoke. 'Don't let the wife know how many beers I've had. She goes bananas if I have more than one.'

'So how many beers have you had, Bill?'

'I don't know.'

Sparky groaned. 'If you don't know, how in the Hell do you expect us to know? Oh, Bill, go to sleep.'

At that moment, Bill's plump little Helena stepped out of the accommodation on to the deck where we were sprawled in disarray among the empties. Bill hid his bottle, she smiled at us, but her eyes scanned the contents of the beer crate and noted the half-empty bottle close to Bill's right hand.

'It will soon be time for dinner, Bill. We will go and get ready. Shall we? And you need a fresh shirt, dear. Come along, dear.'

She had pushed her face down close to his and her words were dribbling with ice. It was not a request, it was an order and he knew it. She hoisted him to his feet and almost frog-marched him to their cabin. We heard the door closing in spite of the heat in the accommodation.

Some time passed. We had returned to our cold beers, idle conversation and hoping for a cool breeze, when Bill came floundering out of the accommodation and flopped down to squat beside us. His shirt was soaked in sweat and incorrectly buttoned, his flies were still undone and he looked as if he had just completed a four-minute mile in a rain storm.

'Damn you, Sparky!' He whined as he struggled for breath and threw a paperback book at him. 'Damn you. In future, keep your bliddy, lousy, dirty sexy books away from my wife.'

WHEN THE CAPTAIN CRIED

W e were lying at anchor waiting to go in to Madras, and Madras being Madras, our cabin doors were open, our portholes were open, our cabin fans were running flat out and still the sweat oozed out of our pores. We had heard of many ships that had air-conditioning but we were not in their league in those far-off days.

Old Captain Jones appeared at my cabin door in uniform shorts, vest, flip-flops and a towel round his shoulders. On an old man, it was not a pleasant sight.

'Hello, Bob. I've just heard about your book where you met up with a big shark. In Indonesia, wasn't it?'

'Aye, Captain. A big shark and a flimsy dug-out canoe.'

I flipped the top off a nice, lukewarm beer, held it out and since I had flipped the top off, he didn't refuse. He came in and sat down. 'Aye, Bob, I liked it. Hell, it gave me goose pimples. Where did you learn to write?'

'I didn't learn to write, Captain. It is something that happens. If you can tell a good story by talking your head off after a few beers, why not write it down? Or imagine your readers are deaf mutes. Write the first sentence, first paragraph, first page etcetera and keep going until you've told the story. Easy.'

He considered this for a few minutes. 'And you just use your imagination?'

'That's one way, Captain, or you just use your memory. I still remember every second I was in that dugout canoe with that big shark following the two of us and that twit of a Chief Engineer talking about football. He only glimpsed it once and said it must be a porpoise, then he went back to talking about the time West Ham beat Liverpool in the cup. I can still get goose pimples when I remember it.'

'When you remember the shark or West Ham beating Liverpool?'

We laughed, then sat quietly, content with each other's company and finished our beers. Well, they were Asahi beers in small bottles that only lasted a few minutes.

'You make it all sound so easy, Bob. I've a story I'd like to write someday, something that happened a long time ago.' He paused. 'I suppose it is one story in two parts.....'

He stopped and the only sound we could hear was the whirring of my cabin fan and the slow whine and thump of the boiler feed pump five decks below.

'Well, let's have something that might help to get your story started.' I reached into the cupboard at the end of my bunk, brought out my one and only full litre of Bell's and took two glasses from my bookshelf. I poured two large measures and handed him one.

'This will help you to get your story started. Start talking, Captain, tell me your story.'

He studied the whisky in his glass for a moment and then took a large swallow. 'I think I need to tell this story to someone. It has been swilling around in my head for years and I've never told anyone, not a soul except those in the medical staff in the Dreadnought Hospital Psychiatric Ward. You tell me how to write it.'

'Start by taking your time. Get the picture of what happened clear in your head. When it's clear, start talking.'

He did take his time, stared at my deck head for a while and then started talking quietly.

'It was 1946. We left Tilbury, discharged some cargo in Capetown and were heading for Mauritius when we got a radio message that an aeroplane had crashed in the sea somewhere ahead of us. But messages could be brief and quite indistinct in those days. However, the sea was dead calm and we went flat out to see if we could help to find it. We expected it to be somewhere between us and Mauritius. Flat out? We could only do seven knots in that old bucket and she belched a helluva lot of black smoke from the funnel doing it.'

Then he went quiet again so I sat back and waited. Suddenly he drained his glass of whisky and held it out to me. I poured him another large measure and he sat looking into it to see if his story was there. 'We found we were only a few miles from where the plane came down and there was no sign of it. There were, however, about ten or twelve bodies in lifejackets, floating in a dead calm sea and waving to us, but nothing else. We slowed and stopped and it only took seconds to get a lifeboat down into the water. The Mate, two ABs and I got in and we rowed over to the bodies.'

He took another swallow but now his hand was shaking and his voice was now down to a whisper. 'The nearest casualty reached out and held on to the lifeboat and I gripped his hand to haul him on board. The man screamed; 'No! Leave us. Shoals of barracudas have eaten the bottom halves of our bodies. They've eaten our legs off. They've eaten everything from the waist down. There are only our top halves left and we are waiting for the sharks to arrive. The sharks will finish us off quickly. Just go back to your ship. Stay away from us.' Then he pushed himself away. It was then I could see there was nothing, no body, no legs below his lifejacket, just flashes of barracudas in dark red cloudy water.'

Suddenly the Captain shuddered violently and dropped his whisky glass. I closed my cabin door, picked up the glass and poured him another in readiness. He closed his eyes and clenched his teeth hard. Slowly his shaking stopped.

'I had gripped that man's hand to haul him into the lifeboat but he sobbed: 'No! Leave us. We don't want you. We are waiting for the sharks. They'll be along soon when they smell the blood.' That was a long time ago and sometimes I can still feel his cold wet hand in my grip, I can still see his face as he looked up at me and said 'No, we don't want you.' I remember the agony on his face when he said it.'

We sat without moving or speaking. His face had gone chalk white and haggard and his eyes looked wild as it all came back to him.

'Then the first of the sharks came......'

He put one hand up over his eyes then used his towel to wipe his face. I thought he was going to faint and slide off my settee and I got ready to grab him.

Minutes passed slowly and he recovered.

When he was calm, he dried his face and put the towel down. 'I've never told anyone this before. I knew I would get in a bloody mess if I tried. I'm sorry, Bob. I can still see that man's face. I can still feel his hand in mine.'

'Drink up, you need another anaesthetic.' I held up the Bell's.

He hesitated but I sat with my arm out and the bottle poised, ready to pour and he did hold his glass out. I gave him another stiff measure and the level in my Bell's bottle was going down quite steadily.

'I was a mass of jangled nerves because of what happened that day. I wasn't right in the head so they stuck me in a hospital in Mauritius for a while then flew me to London accompanied by a male nurse with hypodermics. I had about ten days in the Dreadnought Merchant Navy Hospital in Greenwich (bless them) where they filled me up with more tranquilisers, more injections and kept a straitjacket in the cupboard beside me. Eventually, they said it was OK to go home.'

He swilled his whisky round in his glass for a few minutes then looked at me. 'But there were times, Bob, when I was not OK.'

Again he was silent for a while as if debating something within himself. I felt he no longer remembered I was there.

To bring him back to reality I murmured softly. 'Just take your time, Captain.'

'I'll take my time. I'll take my time.' He sighed deeply. 'They gave me a train ticket to get me home to Kingussie. It was early evening when I took a taxi up to London's Kings Cross station. The train was 'The Royal Highlander', and every Scot going home knows it well. It has many assets.'

His memory was now working well and I knew he could 'see' every detail of things that happened in those far-off days.

'One of its assets is that anyone who books a sleeper compartment is allowed to sit in a first-class compartment. Well, who wants to go to bed at eight-thirty? So I found an empty first-class compartment next to the sleepers and settled in with my newspaper. A woman came in. No, Bob, I'll correct that. Not a woman. She was a very beautiful lady actually, and she had two small suitcases.'

'Allow me?' I took them from her and placed them on the overhead rack. As soon as I had accomplished this mean feat, we smiled and sat facing each other. I returned to reading my newspaper.

'You are very kind. Thank you,' she smiled.

'The Royal Highlander' was starting to move when a girl opened the compartment door and struggled in with a large suitcase. She was trying to put it on the rack beside our suitcases when the ticket collector came hurrying up behind her.

'I am sorry, miss, but this is a first-class compartment. Your ticket is third class.'

'But I want to be in a first-class compartment,' she snorted indignantly.

He repeated, 'I am sorry, but your ticket is for third-class.'

He then reached for her suitcase, took her by the arm and ushered her down the corridor towards third class. I closed the compartment door behind them and sat down again.

The lady and I smiled at each other again then she spoke. 'I don't understand. You very kindly assisted me with my suitcases. Yet you didn't help that young girl with hers. May I ask why?'

'Why? Because you are a lady and you are therefore entitled to be treated as a lady. That girl was not, and never would be, a lady.'

'Our conversation carried on from there, Bob, and I did the stupidest thing I ever did in my whole life. My treatment in the Dreadnought involved giving all the details of how I acted and re-acted to finding the victims of the plane crash and what happened there. They asked clinical questions and I answered them vaguely. I gave doctors, specialists, nurses, psychologists some of the details when I was injected up to the eyeballs with tranquilisers, drugs, medicines of all kinds and stuffed full of pills, but I couldn't put the sheer horror of what happened into words. They quizzed me when I was floating in a dream world.'

He leaned back and closed his eyes and I wondered if he was going to sleep. I reached for the Bells and let the neck of the bottle rattle against his glass as I poured.

His eyes opened to check the level in his glass. A pause, then he continued. 'I started talking and found myself telling her the whole story in great detail. I don't know why, but it just seemed important I should tell that lady. I had to tell someone and I told her everything. I'm ashamed to say my eyes had filled with tears then I noticed this lovely lady was crying too. She took my hand, the hand that had held the poor chap in the life jacket and kissed the palm gently and sympathetically. We gazed deeply into each others eyes then suddenly kissed each other. Our passion increased, our kisses became long hot passionate kisses and we clung to each other's bodies. We stumbled into my sleeper berth, locked the door and made love all night......

He placed the empty whisky glass on my desk and stood up, swaying slightly. 'Well, Bob, do you think I should publish it?'

'Captain, you can remember all the details clearly, so why not?'

'Remember all the details?' He wiped his eyes and laughed. 'Bob, I've been making that story up – Hic! - since this ship left Tilbury six weeks ago. I reckoned that if a bliddy Second Engineer can write a book about sharks, ships and screwing lovely ladies, so can a bliddy Captain. Goodnight, Bob. And thanks – Hic! - for the whiskies.'

Still laughing, he left, closing my cabin door quietly behind him and leaving me sitting with a large unfinished whisky still in my hand.

Then I began to recap on all he had told me and weighed against what I knew of the man. How much of his story was true, how much was fiction? If it was fiction, fiction he said he had written since we left Tilbury six weeks earlier, why did he cry in telling me? Or did he cry because every word of his story was true and he still lived with the horror of it?

I know the man. I know the answer.

TULIPS FOR A LADY

She was an enormous seven-cylinder, fourstroke, turbo-blown Diesel with a million faults. Another of the engine room's endearing virtues was that her Diesel generators were an experimental and totally unsuccessful design that was never fitted in any other ships. After three horrific years, her owners could no longer find engineers who could be persuaded to sail in her. Lying unwanted in Immingham Dock, her asking price kept falling as the weeks became months and after a two-year wait of lying idle, our shipping company bought her.

We joined and, as a token gesture, the company had a repair squad on board for a few days. Then the day came when we were expected to sail.

'Right, Bob. 'Stand By' is at eight o'clock tonight, so, after breakfast, I suggest we put the lads on watches,' boomed Al Savage, our Chief Engineer. 'We'll kick over the engine before lunch, just to make sure she starts, and then do nothing until 'Stand By'. How does that sound to you?' I am, to this day, grateful for the fact that Al Savage was our Chief Engineer.

It sounded OK to me. However the main engine refused to co-operate at the predetermined time of eleven o'clock that morning. At eight o'clock in the evening she reluctantly fired on one cylinder and many minutes passed before she began firing on another one.

The Chief grabbed the phone and frantically called the bridge.

'Cast off! We're moving!'

By the time the engine was firing on some of the seven cylinders, we were gagging and choking in the smoke and thick fumes that filled the engine room. I was on the controls and my eyes were streaming so much I could hardly see the pressure gauges in front of me.

We didn't stop to drop the pilot – we were too afraid we might not manage to get her started again and the bridge had to be content with a slight reduction in speed. Our Captain informed us later that the pilot resorted to performing a most daring leap from the Jacob's ladder to land flat out onto the roof of the pilot launch.

But we did stop on our way to Casablanca; nineteen times, to be precise. A few more ports round the Mediterranean, with so many breakdowns and major overhauls on each trip that the Chief suddenly decided he'd had enough and left us in Palermo.

It was there that the new Chief joined with his wife. They were newly-weds, both still in their twenties and anticipating the trip would be like some kind of honeymoon cruise. His wife was excitedly unpacking their suitcases in their cabin while he and I 'talked shop' out on deck.

'I had a call from Head Office in London,' he informed me. 'Evidently we leave here for Antwerp. There's a mountain of spare parts there and a shore squad to do some of the heavy work.'

'Aye, Chief, that's nice. Did Head Office tell you about the state of the engines and generators when we took over? Or about the number of breakdowns we've had? I'll let you have a wee read of my workbook. It'll scare the daylights out of you. It reads like a horror comic, honestly. And the lads have been working like madmen since we left Immingham and they need a break. But you'll soon see for yourself. They're walking around like zombies.'

As Second Engineer I have to assess what work has to be done against how fit my fellow engineers are to do it. Shipping Companies are not the least bit interested if engineers have been working more than a hundred hours a week every week to keep the ship moving. Some Chiefs are afraid of their jobs and afraid of what the Company might say, but this one was not.

I was digging in my heels, quietly but firmly. 'I don't want to work them any more until they've had a break in Antwerp – and that goes for the donkeymen as well.'

His face tightened as I enlightened him about what we'd been through since Immingham.

He said, very slowly, 'Bob, I don't believe in engineers working overtime for nothing for a bugger that's already a millionaire.'

All this from a young Chief! Blessings upon the man!

The engines had improved considerably but there was still a nightmare load of work to be done.

Three piston ring changes done at sea, and when each one- ton piston has to be taken out through the crankcase on chain blocks it is not funny. Fourteen burned-out exhaust and inlet valves replaced were all part of the nightmare. Long hours in the engine room made us unsure if it was night time or daytime up top.

We arrived in Antwerp at noon. Not in the usual docks normally frequented by reputable shipping companies, but a few miles further on, in a little backwater surrounded by narrow cobbled streets, gas lighting and 'olde worlde' houses built two hundred years earlier. Literally, a port from the dark ages.

Big Bill, the Senior Third Engineer, had spent most of the night working on one of 'his' Diesel generators yet still found time to give a hand on 'Stand By.' When they rang 'Finished with Engines', I assumed everyone would stagger to the shower and collapse in their bunks.

'Bob,' exclaimed Bill, our six-foot three-inch beanpole of a Third Engineer, 'I'm too tired to sleep, too tired and too sore. I'm going ashore to look for a nice quiet beer somewhere.'

Sleep is difficult when the agony of acute exhaustion takes over. Your mind goes to sleep but your body twitches and thrashes about, arms flailing, legs kicking until you wake yourself up again. Bill was giving his painful body a chance to calm itself before he went to his bunk.

We caught up with him in the first bar we came to eight hours later and the buxom blonde barmaid was pleased to flash her false teeth at us as we entered.

I called. 'Beers all round, madam, and if any of us says you look beautiful, please accept it that we have had too much to drink and throw us out. I only hope you don't speak English.'

'I speak better English than you do, Scottie. I come from Liverpool!' She beamed cheerfully at all of us. 'Beers all round?'

Someone once said that if you don't allow yourself to get thirsty, you don't know the true pleasure of a drink. It's also true that if you don't thrash your body to the pinnacles of complete exhaustion you don't really know the sheer luxury of sitting down. Taking the weight off your legs and your back for a little while is heavenly. We sat quite still and surveyed the dimly lit bar with its smoky oak beams, bottles, and jugs and assorted glasses on display. Tired smiles were exchanged with the barmaid and her two local Belgian customers.

So we had some beers and were quietly accepting all the misfortunes that the world sometimes bestows on British Merchant Navy Engineer Officers when the bar door opened and an elderly local gentleman entered, carrying bunches of tulips for sale. We surveyed him too.

'You know, lads, this new Chief's a good bloke,' I said.

There were a nodding of heads and murmurs of agreement from all hands.

'And,' I went on, 'his wife is a little darling too. Always ready with a big sympathetic smile for any of us.'

More mutters of agreement, more nodding of heads.

'Well, I think I'll take her back some flowers,' I concluded, smacking my hand on the bar counter for emphasis.

There were cries of 'me too,' from all of them and hands dived into pockets to buy the old man's tulips. Though none of us wanted to be outdone by the others, we hadn't realised that he had a barrow load of tulips parked at the pub door. Nevertheless, we bought every last tulip in the cart and the little old Belgian flower seller made off with the best bit of business he'd done since his grandfather was a boy.

We were very pleased with us.

Bill had an angelic smile on his face when his eyes slowly closed and he slumped over backwards to land flat out on the bar room floor. Heads turned and looked at him in mild curiosity to see what he'd do next.

There are many men who exist in a world of desks and offices, of forty-hour weeks and afternoon tea, who are dressed in serge suits and wear ties and that is a narrow existence of a life. To us, they are only touching the edges of living. Most Merchant Navy officers can live comfortably and be respected at every level in society, at ease with everyone from the aristocracy to the dregs.

Minutes passed. With a sigh I finished my beer, stood him up and slung him over my left shoulder in a fireman's lift.

'Pass me my tulips.'

I was handed my tulips.

'And Bill's.'

I was handed Bill's tulips.

'Can you take mine as well?' They all cried out simultaneously and loaded me with their tulips as they spoke. I had one arm wrapped round Bill and the other clutching a great haystack of tulips I couldn't see over when I headed out the door.

Bill was getting heavier with each step and every time I eased him into a more comfortable carrying position, I spilled some tulips. Eventually, enough tulips fell to a point where I could see where I was going and both hands could then reach and grip each other.

I reasoned that if I stopped and put Bill down, I couldn't pick him up with one arm still full of tulips. Similarly, if I put the tulips down, I couldn't pick them up with one arm still full of Bill. So I staggered on until I reached the ship.

There, my troubles multiplied. The gangway rose at an angle of sixty degrees and its lower end lay eighteen inches from ground level. When I stepped up those eighteen inches, Bill's chin hooked on the end and pulled me off again. I bent forward, I bent back, I tried everything except handstands but Bill's head still banged on the gangway.

I stopped for breath and quietly surveyed the tulips strewn around me. Finally, tired and exasperated, I gritted my teeth and lunged forward and upward with Bill's head smacking every step of the way. Crossing the floodlit deck unseen, into the engineer's accommodation, unlocking Bill's cabin door with my passkey, I finally and thankfully draped our Senior Third Engineer Officer out on his bunk.

I switched on his cabin light and that was when I saw his face. It was a mass of black and blue lumps and bumps and a little blood-splattered in places. Very unlike the suave gentle Bill we all knew and loved so well. I took off his shoes, put out the light and left his cabin on tip-toe.

Next morning, before breakfast I passed the word around the others. 'Don't call Bill, let him have a decent sleep. He's earned it.'

We were finishing breakfast when the duty mess room door opened and Bill staggered in. He pointed to the lumps, bumps and bruises on his face and scowled at us.

'See this, eh? See this? Well, there were four of them, four big Belgian buggers and I gave them a bigger hiding than they gave me! I beat them up solid! So you lot just watch what you say!'

I, for one, said nothing and carried on with my breakfast.

And the Chief's wife was thrilled with her tulips. The five that remained of the bunch.

THE TEA ROOM

'So you see, Mr Seenan, your insurance policy does not cover the lounge ceiling falling down and killing your cat.' The plump little Mr Bell stood with his chin up, his client's folder on his left arm and his ball point pen raised high for emphasis.

'Damn you, sir, what have I been paying for all these years? I mean, even when I was at sea for months on end and the house was lying empty, I paid your damned house insurance. All my neighbours keep an eye on it too. And another thing, your insurance company demanded I fit all kinds of burglar alarms and fancy lights because the house would be empty for months while I'm at sea and they cost a packet. Then after they were fitted you found that I always shut the water and electrics off before I go back to sea. So how can the burglar alarms and your fancy lights work if there's no electricity? You just wouldn't listen!'

'Just an oversight on our part, Mr Seenan, just an oversight.'

'An oversight that cost me eighty pounds. Your oversight, but it's me that had to pay. Now my ceiling has come down and you don't want to know.'

'Mr Seenan, the reason your ceiling came down...'

'...and killed my cat.'

'...And killed your cat, was due to a water leak from a pipe in your attic some time ago. That was negligence on your part and your policy doesn't cover any damage caused by the householder's negligence.'

'Good Heavens, man, that leak occurred twelve years ago and it was repaired! The ceiling didn't come down twelve years ago. It came down last week!'

'I regret to say that the time difference is of very little consequence. You'll find that on page one hundred and sixty two of your policy, paragraph five, subsection ...'

'Mr Bell, forget it. I'm disgusted. You're not the least bit interested in paying out on the policy.'

'That's not the right attitude, Mr Seenan. I had a long tiring journey getting here by bus. It took me through every village in Yorkshire and seemed to stop at every lamppost. Evidently there isn't a railway station within a hundred miles of here.' He picked up his brief case and umbrella. 'I'm sorry you're disappointed with our services but ...'

Mr Seenan turned his back on his guest and a gleam came in his eye. 'You came by bus, did you, and about ten miles by taxi? Little-Hole-in-the-Moor does have a railway station,' he said softly, interrupting his visitor's flow. 'Neat little station it is, too.'

'Really?'

'About fifteen miles from here. Oh, come on, pick up your things. I'll get the car out and take you there for I'll be glad to see the back of you.'

A few minutes later they set off in Mr Seenan's car to the railway station and parted without a 'good-bye' from either gentleman.

Mr Bell always had a nice cup of tea in the afternoon when he was in the office. His client's sullen departure, depositing him in front of the railway station in one of Yorkshire's tiniest hamlets was not going to change that. His victory, for Mr Bell considered the saving of his insurance company's money by fair means or foul, was indeed a victory, earning him the right to his cup of tea. He would not forget to put it on his expense account either.

He carried his rolled umbrella and brief case with the same aplomb a British Field Marshall would carry his baton, and thus armed, Mr Bell entered the railway station tea room at Little Hole-in-the-Moor.

Once inside, he found tables that normally sat four had been pushed together to form one table large enough to accommodate a dozen customers. Those seated there were chatting amiably and all had writing pads and pens before them.

He made his way to the counter and it was a few minutes before a plump little blond lady arrived to serve him.

'One cup of tea, please.' His gaze turned to the array of delicacies on the counter. His successful afternoon made him feel in a reckless mood, financially. 'And I think I may just have one of your cream scones also.'

The plump little blond looked him over and gave him her brightest smile as she poured out a cup of tea.

'Poetry class,' she whispered.

'Pardon?'

'Big competition. Prize £10. Poems about unusual objects this week.'

'I see. Thank you.' He made his way to a vacant table where he could observe the contestants.

The voice of the chairwoman at the head of the big table was heard above the chattering.

'Quiet, please. Thank you. You, Ellen, yes dear, you're next.' The other voices faded into silence.

A frizzled little woman rose, opened a long box and took out an ostrich feather. She held it up for all to see.

'Ostrich feather. This was a present I got many years ago from my sister in Capetown, not the one who married the pig farmer, the other one who married the ....'

The chairwoman groaned. 'Get on with it, Ellen, please.'

'Er, yes. Well, here it is.' She cleared her throat and began:

'Watch this genuine ostrich feather,
Used to forecast our coming weather,
If it's wet, t'will surely snow,
If it moves, strong winds will blow,

If it's damp, there's rain about,
And if it's hot, the sun is out.'

The poem met with polite applause and
nods of approval from the others.

The leader smiled. 'Yes, Ellen, very good,
very good indeed. Maybe it needs a teeny-weeny
bit of polishing. But very good. Now Maisie, do
you have something?'

The lady referred to was fumbling down
inside the neck of her woolly jumper when the
chairwoman spoke to her.

'It's just an itch. It bothered me a lot last
night. My Herbert said.....'

'I meant something to read out? A poem
about an unusual object? Remember?'

'Oh, yes. My poem. Something what I
wrote myself in bed. Shall I read it out?'

Mr Bell was conscious of the tutor's
inward groan. His cream scone lay untouched on
the plate but he had finished his tea.

The lady referred to as 'Maisie' looked
around the ring of faces at the table before
reading from a crinkled sheet of paper.

'I wonder where my wages went?
Within the week my money's spent,
All is gone, from bad to worse,
Not a coin stays in my purse,
Except this old bent 50p,
That my dear husband gave to me.'

She looked at the others shyly and sat down amid another modest round of applause. She passed a bent 50 pence piece round the others for their inspection. Each confirmed it was indeed a 50 pence piece and it certainly was well bent. That was the last poem to be read so the class rose to leave, gathered their paraphernalia and made their way out.

At this point Mr Bell also rose to his feet and, taking his empty cup to the counter, requested another cup of tea.

The plump little blonde smiled coyly at him. 'I never charge for the second cup.'

'Very kind. Though I'm surprised to find a poetry group in a railway station tea room,' he remarked. 'Pleasantly surprised.'

'They often come here. They're from the HIRST.'

'The HIRST?'

'Yes. The HIRST: 'The Home for Retired School Teachers.' You see, when lady schoolteachers retired they were at a loss as to what to do with their lives, especially if they were spinsters or widows. A gentleman who owned a shipping company donated one of his large houses to selected lady schoolteachers when he died, in memory of his dear departed wife. Our Mr Seenan is a Chief Engineer in that shipping company. He is in charge.'

She walked to the window to watch the others leave.

'It's getting dark. They are just getting on the bus now. The little school bus is outside round the back and Mr Seenan takes them all home. Sometimes Mr Seenan, sometimes one of the ladies drives the bus. I think I'll join you in a cup of tea, if you don't mind. I've been on my feet all day.'

The poetry class had now gone and silence reigned. The plump little blonde joined Mr Bell at his table and sat beside him.

Mr Bell was suddenly very aware of the fact that he was alone in the railway station waiting room with a blonde lady.

'My name is Maria,' she smiled and leaned over to put her hand on his knee.

He tensed. 'Is it?' He moved his knee away from her and coughed nervously.

'And you are Mr Bell of Ensun Bartholomew Insurance Company. Tell me about it.'

He coughed again. 'How did you know my name?'

'I was talking with Joe Seenan. He brought the bus to take the others home and Joe and I had a few minutes together. He told me about you and your insurance. We all love Joe Seenan.'

'Yes, well, Mr Seenan is insured by my company, Ensun Bartholomew Insurance Company. It is a good company to work for. I had to see your Mr Seenan about his house insurance. It was an important matter and I had to be very careful.'

She breathed and moved closer to him. 'Mr Seenan is a Chief Engineer Officer in the

Merchant Navy. He's a very clever man. We all love Joe Seenan.' She emphasised the word 'love.'

'I was not allowed to tell you his name,' he stuttered.

Maria pouted her lips, 'You told me his name when I sat down with you five minutes ago. I was not allowed to give you that free cup of tea, but I did.'

Mr Bell considered this, looked round the waiting room to make sure they were alone.

'And what happened, Mr Bell?'

'Mr Seenan tried to claim money from my insurance company but I tricked him out of it,' he whispered proudly, but moved away a little more. 'I saved my company some money. That's what I call being clever.'

'But our Joe is a very clever man, too. A Chief Engineer in the Merchant Navy has very high qualifications, probably as much as a doctor. The ladies all know Joe. Can I tell you some of the things he has done here in Little-Hole-in-the-Moor? He persuaded British Rail to allow us the use of the station waiting room for the HIRST poetry class and other groups, like the boy scouts, the Saturday Whist Drives and all kinds of meetings. Because the station is a little way out of Hole-in-the-Moor, he bought a lovely second hand bus to get us from the town to the station and back and he, personally, keeps that bus in good order. The bus is insured for any member of the Poetry Group to drive it.'

She moved nearer to Mr Bell who was now leaning away from her at an awkward angle. She slid her hand higher on his leg for a moment, and then stood up, as if she was going to climb on top of him. He cringed away from her and she sat down again.

'Mr Seenan is a wonderful man. He is a Chief Engineer in the Merchant Navy and he goes off to sea for months at a time and that's a lonely, lonely life for a bachelor. There are many ladies in this village who welcome him home, if you see what I mean.'

She sighed, took away the tea things, locked up the little pantry and opened the back door to let him out. When she came out minutes later she was wearing a crash helmet and gauntlets. It was then he saw the scooter standing against the wall.

'Er, Maria? What time is the next train, please?'

'Joe bought me this scooter and looks after it for me. He gave it to me because I volunteered to do the teas. I do other things for him too, if you know what I mean. He is very generous.'

Mr Bell raised his voice. 'When is the next train, woman?'

'Joe is a Chief Engineer Officer in the Merchant Navy and sometimes when he joins a ship he takes one of us along with him as his wife. Senior officers are allowed to take wives along so some of us take turns at being his wife and go on a cruise with him. We think of it as a prize in the poetry competitions. One of the best prizes, actually. I've had a three-month trip with Joe. We went to New York and Havana and Jamaica and Mexico and Buenos Aires and home again. Wonderful!' She sighed as the memories came back.

'But what do people in Little-Hole-in –the –Moor say?'

'Wives are not allowed on cruises with him, Joe won't allow that, and those that do go on a trip with Joe are carefully chosen. Others hear about them, but they are not deprived of anything if you see what I mean,' she giggled.

Mr Bell panicked when Maria fastened her crash helmet and turned her scooter round.

'When is the next train?' he screamed, stumbling after her.

One kick, and her scooter roared into life. 'Didn't our lovely Joe Seenan tell you? A Mister Beeching closed lots of railways thirty years ago and this was one of them. So good-bye, Mr Bell, and don't you ever be unkind to our darling Joe Seenan again. In fact, don't you ever be unkind to any Merchant Navy Chief Engineer Officers again or you will have us to deal with. G'bye!'

She drove off into the night.

He watched the scooter's little red light disappear into the distance and Mr Bell knew there were not going to be any trains.

BLUE and PERRY

'Blue' was the first budgerigar I ever had on board ship. He was tame from the day I bought him, readily accepting me as a companion and quite content to be on board. His cage in the Singapore market was tiny and at floor level in a small dark shop and I bought him a cage big enough for him to move about in.

I could tell he was not a young bird from the white, unlined forehead and the blue cere at the top of his beak showed he was a male. On his first day out of the cage, he had to learn how to fly – a sign that he had been in a small cage all his life and I could feel his sheer exhilaration at having freedom to spread his wings, to fly around in.

When anyone came into my cabin, Blue would immediately leave his cage and fly to my shoulder to observe the intruder. But he rarely flew to their shoulders. He treated them all with a great deal of suspicion until he knew them.

Our Second Mate, Paddy was thrilled to bits when Blue eventually accepted him as a friend, so when the opportunity presented itself, he dashed ashore to the native market in Chang Alley in Singapore and bought himself a budgerigar. He named it 'Smoky'. But Paddy's Smoky sulked. It didn't want to know anyone, it seldom moved from the end of the spar in the cage. It just sulked.

I took Blue to visit Smoky but when we put them together in the same cage, Blue chirped and jumped around and tried to cheer Smoky up, tried to be friendly but Smoky just hung his head and turned his back on him. So, Blue and I gave up and retreated to our own cabin.

'I know what's wrong with Smoky!' Paddy burst into my cabin one day, all excited. 'I'm sure I know what's wrong with him. He needs a mate! I'll get him a wife, a young good-looking female.'

So, an excited Paddy dashed ashore to Chang Alley when the opportunity arose and returned with a bright green 'Sexy Lexy'. Smoky was immediately very interested in this attractive female now taking up residence with him in his cage and he immediately tried to have his evil way with her, but it was not to be. When he moved near her she pecked his head, battered him with her wings and knocked him off the perch. If he persisted, she beat him up until he was a tangled mass of feathers in a corner at the bottom of the cage while she reigned aloof and alone on the perch above him.

'Let's try her with Blue.'

That was Captain Mel Cooper's suggestion so we three trooped off to my cabin with an indignant Sexy Lexy in a box.

We entered the cabin; Blue flew out of his cage, straight to my shoulder and stared at

Captain Cooper and Paddy. When Paddy let this highly indignant Sexy Lexy out of the box she flew round the cabin and I think Blue's eyes nearly popped out of his head. He raced after the wench, circling the cabin but keeping high above her, and then crash dived straight down on top of her when she was over my bunk. The bold Blue spread her wings wide apart and had his evil way with her while we three stood and applauded.

Then he returned to my shoulder, jumping up and down, chirping merrily and accepting all praise.

Paddy picked up his listless Sexy Lexy and took her back to the cage in his cabin. When she had a few minutes to recover, she jumped up and beat the daylights out of poor Smoky.

Fourteen months later I went home on leave and left Blue in the tender care of Captain Mel Cooper, Chief Engineer Mac Dryden, Chief Mate Davy Stewart, and one dejected Paddy. I never heard a word from any of them again but I'll always remember them and my pal Blue.

A year or two went by and I was requested to join the M.V. Ribot somewhere up in the Persian Gulf. Since I had arrived a day early I wandered round the town looking at the shops and, lucky me, I found a pet shop displaying a large cage packed full of assorted budgerigars. To me, one bird stood out from all the others, a fine young cock with a proud head and beautiful blue feathers. I bought him.

It was quite a long pantomime watching two highly exasperated Arab shop assistants using nets at the end of long handles trying to fob me off with any bird they managed to trap in their nets. Eventually their perseverance was rewarded and I had the young cock bird I had selected. He was a good choice.

But there was an unexpected bonus awaiting both of us.

The Chief Engineer, Kevin P. O'Mahoney, had his young wife on board, a lovely lady with a soft Irish accent. Budgies readily respond to a female voice and Audrey had a sweet Irish voice. So this young couple inherited Perry for a couple of months until the time came when they left to go home to Cork then I had him back again.

But Audrey had taught Perry to talk beautifully! The others said he could talk better than they could and he learned new phrases very quickly. He had become a 'show off' and he loved having an audience.

Kevin O'Mahoney was one of the finest chiefs I ever sailed with in my forty-one years at sea and his lovely Audrey was a great asset to him. They were both great assets to Perry. It was a sad day for Perry and me when they waved their good-byes.

So Perry quite cheerfully accepted this new world in the Second Engineer's cabin - but there were problems. At sea in hot weather, with no modern luxuries like air-conditioning, cabin doors are left open and curtains are used to cover the entrances to the cabins. When my fellow officers knew I was 'down below' or elsewhere, they would put their heads round the door curtain and teach Perry new phrases, phrases that crackled and turned the air bright blue. His new repertoire would have embarrassed a Liverpool docker or made a Glasgow hooligan blush.

He loved the reaction he got with this new vocabulary, a reaction he didn't get when he said, quote; 'Who's a pretty boy, then?'

This new repertoire got results and pleased him immensely.

We had a routine at his bath time. I would run some water into the washbasin and place my big sponge in it. Perry would become excited and fly down on to the sponge, splash around in the water then shake himself dry. When satisfied, he would return to the cage and this routine included going through the repertoire of his choice phrases.

Then my Mary joined the ship. Climbing our gangway meant she had to wash her hands immediately she came into the cabin. Perry studied this newcomer carefully as he did with all strangers. Then Mary ran the water into the washbasin and Perry began the repertoire he had been taught by our fellow officers.

She staggered backwards amazed and flopped down on the settee that fortunately happened to be behind her. She had never heard a bird speak before. She had never heard such language before either! But Mary soon tolerated it, though Perry did make her blush at times.

When we went home on leave at the end of that contract, there were no shortage of volunteers to look after Perry and we like to think he missed Mary and me just as much as we missed him.

And we certainly missed him.

OUTRAGE

We were on a twelve-month charter to sail from Japan to Australia with a lovely 30% 'good will' cash bonus. In those far off halcyon days, a one pound note was worth one thousand and eighty yen and Japan was a seafarer's paradise.

Loading in Japan took three glorious weeks and discharging in Australia took five weeks, long enough for tired souls to recuperate from our three weeks in Japan. Our crew consisted of six European Officers, seven Chinese Officers and a crew of thirty-eight Chinese. Some of the Chinese had been four years on the ship and life was easy for all. The engine room was a showpiece where everything gleamed.

Our owner, with his wife and sons, sometimes visited when the ship was in Hong-Kong, and sea life is very different when you're working for a family you can talk to and swop stories with.

Long stays in port with a Chinese staff of two Thirds, two Fourths, one Electrician, two fitters, eight donkeymen/greasers and about six cleaners kept everything washed, polished and painted. On one occasion, five Australian nurses in uniform were given a tour of the engine room and were amazed at its cleanliness. Sometimes we could spend an afternoon kicking a ball around or going for a walk around town. But our engine room was maintained beautifully and we were proud of it.

Then we arrived in Moji, in Japan. We'd only just tied up alongside when the Captain and the Chief wanted to see me. The Japanese shipping agent was with them.

'Right, Bob, the Second Engineer on the 'Staffcourt' has been hurt and they need a Second right away. She's in Yokohama. Okay with you?'

'Sure, no problems.' When you are on super high wages plus bonuses and part of a sea-going staff that are a respected cog in the business, you don't say 'no' to anything.

A couple of hours later I was travelling to Yokohama, first class, at something well over a hundred miles an hour on one of Japan's famous 'Honshu Bullet' trains. On arrival in Yokohama, I was met by another agent who took me to the 'Staffcourt' and left me with my suitcases at the bottom of the gangway. Normally the agent would 'deliver' me straight to the Captain but this one left me without a backward glance.

Another abnormality was the seaman on gangway duty would have found someone to carry my suitcases on board. I subsequently carried them on board myself and the seaman on the gangway was not to be seen anywhere.

Knocking on the door marked 'Second Engineer Officer' achieved nothing. I tried the handle and the door opened quite easily to offer a cabin littered with paperback books, an assortment of full and empty beer cans in a case and a couple of overflowed ashtrays. The dayroom's two portholes above the daybed were wide open and on the daybed itself was a large dark brown stain of what was obviously dried blood.

I placed my suitcases just inside the door, dropped my coat over them and went to see the Chief Engineer for some information.

I knocked on his door and heard some hurried rustling.

'Who is it?' His voice was whispered behind the door.

'Bob Jackman, new Second Engineer.'

Again a whisper. 'How do I know who you are?'

'For Heaven's sake! Don't bother!' I bellowed and stormed back to the Second's cabin to put on a boilersuit.

The engine room was a scrap yard. Every piece of engineering equipment and auxiliary machinery had oil, steam or water leaks. Nothing had ever been painted, cleaned or polished in months and there was rust on everything that could possibly rust.

In the boiler room, the boiler feed pump moaned and groaned in agony and the fuel pump seemed ready to kick its last. There was a steam leak in the back tubes of the boiler somewhere and both furnaces were choked with clinker.

A Chinese donkeyman stood at the far end of the boiler room, his face wary and menacing like a cornered animal. I walked the length of the boiler room ignoring him, then made my way up top and into the accommodation. I stopped at the door marked 'Third Engineer', knocked once and entered without waiting for a reply.

There were about six of them sitting inside the small cabin making it quite crowded.

'Who is Third Engineer?' I spoke quietly but they heard every syllable.

Eyes turned to look at a bald-headed man in the corner. I stretched out my arm and pointed at him, accusingly, before speaking.

'To-morrow morning at six o'clock, I want all hands in the bottom of the engine room, ready to start work. Do you understand?'

I waited a moment before lowering my hand. They were still silent when I left.

From the Third's cabin it was a short trip upstairs to the Captain's cabin. I was growing angrier by the minute and knocked heavily on his door.

'Yes? Who is it?'

'Bob Jackman, new Second Engineer.'

I heard bolts being drawn, a key turning in the door lock and the door opened.

Captain Burton was in his mid-fifties and looked very much like a Master Mariner. We shook hands and he drew me into his cabin. The door was again locked behind me.

'Well, take a seat, Mister Jackman. What do you think of the 'Staffcourt' so far?'

'Just great! I can see lots of court cases coming up. Supposing somebody can tell me what's been happening here?'

A ship no longer in a seaworthy condition would take a lot of explaining to those in authority. I knew the Captain would need all the allies he could find to keep his own yardarm clear.

'Basically,' he began, 'Second Engineer Kempt hadn't been with Chinese before and thought he could treat them any way he wanted. In fact he treated them like animals. Well, he was a big bloke and even the Chief was afraid of him when he'd had a few beers under his belt. I wanted rid of him but we're on a Bangkok to Yokohama contract with lots of small print and a Thai Government playing funny buggers. No changing of crew members until the end of contract except for medical reasons. Well, the Chinese engine room crowd got together and stuffed hundreds of razor blades into the bristles of a sweeping brush. They must have spent a lot of Japanese yen buying so many. When Kempt was having his afternoon sleep on his daybed they rammed the head of the brush into his face and rubbed it up and down.' The Captain sighed. 'They literally tore his face off and there was blood everywhere. We were at sea and even though they threw the brush over the side, we still picked up lots of safety razor blades off his cabin floor. Dozens! So how many were on the head of the brush?'

We sat quietly for a while, each with our own thoughts.

Then he spoke again. 'I told the Chief Steward to leave the cabin as it is. The Police somewhere might want to see it.'

'Captain, I'd be very happy if you'd have the Chief Steward see my cabin gets cleaned. I want a new mattress on the bunk, another on the settee, all the blood mopped up, clean sheets on the bunk and tell him to get rid of all the rubbish. I'm sleeping in that cabin tonight and I'm not sleeping behind a locked door.'

He frowned and his voice raised a little. 'I don't think you are fully aware of the situation, Mister Jackman.'

'If my cabin isn't cleaned thoroughly, Captain, you can start looking for another Second Engineer.'

This was not bravado or stupidity on my part. I had worked with the Chinese for many years and I knew what I could and couldn't do. Hiding behind a locked door would earn me no bonus points with them. I could see the Captain was worn out and sick of the whole business and my stomach was quivering a little bit, too.

Chinese seamen can change their names as easily as they can change their socks and immediately disappear into the vast crowds of people in Hong Kong and China, never to be seen again. However, under the new regime of the People's Republic of Communist China, if guilty of almost any serious crime they can be put in a prison camp and never heard of again.

I found two stewards giving my cabin a quick clean-up with promises of doing 'proper job' in the morning. Whether it was to remove all evidence or not, I do not know and I was too tired to care. I went into my clean bed and slept with my cabin door unlocked.

I wakened about five-thirty, had a wash and put on a boilersuit. There didn't seem to be anyone else around in the accommodation. The pantry was in the next alleyway and there I found a young pantry boy busy washing some dishes. He smiled nervously at me and immediately reached for a mug and the teapot.

'Tea?'

I nodded and gave him a smile. He poured me a mug of tea and reached for the sugar tin.

'Soo-ga?'

I nodded again. He carefully put in one spoon of sugar and again looked at me again. I held up two fingers and another spoonful of sugar followed the first.

He opened the fridge door, produced a litre of milk and held it up before me. Evidently he didn't know the English word.

'Milk.' I said it clearly.

'Mow-ik.'

'Milk.' I said it slowly and he watched my lips.

'Mi-wik.'

I smiled to encourage him, took the bottle and put a dribble of milk into my mug of tea. It seemed as if I'd just made my first Chinese friend on board. Then I had a spell out on deck in the clear morning air until my watch told me it was six o'clock.

I returned to my cabin, picked up my torch, notebook and pencil and headed for the engine room.

They were all down there, standing silently in a group by the bottom engine room ladder, shuffling their feet uneasily.

'Third, stop the ballast pump and put on the G.S. pump. Strip the ballast pump and fit the spare pump rod.'

'G.S. pump no work. This one piece no good.' His hand lay on the shuttle valve.

'You can fix?'

He nodded. 'Can fix.'

I looked at the Junior Third Engineer. 'Air compressors OK?'

He shook his head. 'Valves long time no good.'

'Can fix?'

'Can fix, do good job.'

And so it went on. From six in the morning we worked until ten o'clock that night with half-hour breaks for breakfast, lunch and dinner and we achieved a lot. Finally it was time to call it a day.

'Okay, Three-o, we start to-morrow morning, six o'clock.'

They had worked almost sixteen hours without a word of complaint and made no objections to doing the same again. The following day was another sixteen-hour spell of hard graft and still no complaints from any of them.

Suddenly there was a new Chief Engineer on board and his predecessor had rapidly left without saying 'goodbye' to anyone.

We shook hands. 'Bill Holtree. What's the job like, Bob?'

Two beers later he had the picture. Then I quizzed him.

'Me? Rose to Chief in Ben Line, married a Chinese girl, joined Hui Ying Engineering and I speak Mandarin Chinese. Now I've come back to sea.'

I thought that was funny. 'As requested by our company's owner?'

'I think he wants the Chinese side of the story.' He studied the last mouthful of beer in his bottle for a few moments. 'If these lads don't get a hearing they'll spend the rest of their lives in a prison camp in the backend of nowhere.'

I liked this man. He looked a bit like Gary Cooper.

We sailed next day for Bangkok. The main engine rattled and clanked, belched smoked like a forest fire and didn't have enough power to pull the skin off a rice pudding. So we stopped at sea on calm days and overhauled the worst of the pistons. I worked hour for hour with the others, something I've always done as Second Engineer.

The 'Staffcourt' was improving daily but it was costing us a fourteen to sixteen hours working day with overhauling and watch keeping. No shoreside breaks in Bangkok, there was always too much work to be done. Thinking back, had a heavy storm hit us in those early days, we would have gone to the bottom in no seconds flat.

The return run to Yokohama was interrupted with a radio message to the Captain from Head Office. 'Proceed Hong Kong for engine room crew change. Awaiting reply.'

The Chief brought the news to me. 'What do you say, Bob?'

'I say let's hear their side of the story. Personally, I don't want to lose them. They're a good bunch of lads. I've been a slave driver and they haven't torn my face to pieces and they've never complained about the hard labour I've put them through. They accept that the work was necessary.'

'I heard that the Second they attacked is disfigured for life.'

We were standing out on the open deck and the Chief had intercepted me as we'd all come up for lunch. The others had walked to the ship's rail to cool off a little.

'Hey! Third!' I turned and beckoned to him to come over. 'Now, Chief, ask him why they assaulted Second Engineer Kempt.'

It took a few minutes before their conversation really got going in Chinese and the Third acted as spokesman for all of them. I sat on the hatch and left them to it. But I could follow most of the indignities and physical abuse our sadistic Mister Kempt had put them through during their months together. A complaint to the last Chief made matters worse, because he didn't want to get involved.

Chief Engineer Holtree walked over to me and stood, rocking to and fro, with his hands in his pockets. Then he looked straight at me. 'That bastard Kempt deserved all he got. You want to keep this squad?'

I nodded. 'Yes, Chief, I want to keep this lot, every damned one of them. They are a good squad.'

'Well, in that case, I better see about getting a message back to the Company. I leave the others to you.'

The others were standing in a group trying to understand what was going on between the Chief and me. They saw him walk off towards the bridge then they turned their attention to me.

'Ship go Hong Kong?' I could almost hear their intakes of breath. They were sure they would all be imprisoned for years, their worst fears were about to be realised.

I took out my notebook and with my pencil at the ready, I asked them. 'Who come back next trip?'

They looked at each other, stunned. 'No go prison?'

'No go prison.'

Suddenly the Third reached out and patted my arm. Then everyone wanted to pat me. I saw more than a few tears of relief among the younger ones. Their months of horror were over and the Owner of our Company would make it right.

Later, in the Chief's cabin, he handed me a sheet of paper 'Thought you might like a copy of the cable I sent to the Company.'

It read : 'Holtree and Jackman unwish crew change'.

'Unwish? That's a new word on me, Chief.'

He took out two beers from his fridge. 'Yes. It's telegraphese. It means we are not going to Hong Kong, we are not changing crew and we've just made a helluva lot of Chinamen happy. So, next question Bob, where is the bliddy bottle opener?'

PENSIONED OFF

I was fifty-three when Scottish Ship Management, my employers for over eight years, informed me that all sea-going personnel over the age of fifty had to have their blood pressure checked. Long hours and hard work had kept me as fit as a butcher's bull terrier so I felt I had no problems when my wife and I motored down from Scarborough to the Shipping Federation Offices in Hull. There, the Merchant Navy doctor checked my blood pressure and seemed delighted to tell me it was too high for anyone serving in the M.N.

It was not too high for anyone in the Armed Forces, Fire Services, Police or others of that ilk, just those in the Merchant Navy. I was soon hospitalised in the Merchant Navy Hospital in Greenwich for a few weeks where they tried to sort me out with an assortment of pills, capsules and a very low calorie diet.

Actually, I found it all quite pleasant. As a Second Engineer Officer it seemed I was the only officer out of almost two dozen patients in our group and I was bestowed with special privileges by those fine gentlemen who were not officers.

For instance, I shared a side ward with two elderly Cunard Line stewards who insisted on serving me at meal times when the food trolleys came round. They scorned the meagre courses recommended by the medical hierarchy for my condition and served me meals that would have graced the tables of the aristocracy. Being stewards, they always had the best of everything in the kitchen and other special treats that were not on patients' menus. The tranquillity of my surroundings had much to do with the lowering of my blood pressure though I did put on a little weight. I stand very much indebted to those two fine gentlemen.

My blood pressure was taken twice daily, morning and evening. The morning reading was higher than the evening reading, due to the morning nurse being young, beautiful and having the kind of beauty that raised blood pressures. The evening nurse was also a lovely lady who was a jovial type that enjoyed being surrounded by seamen.

I felt very well and fit despite being a fifty-three-year old with high blood pressure.

Then one day it all came to an end with a visit by a little doctor at the head of a convoy of nurses and students.

'Aha, yes, Mister Robert Jackman,' boomed the little man. 'Your blood pressure has come down admirably. Yes, admirably. Go home, stay with the medication and allow me the dubious privilege of informing you that you are no longer accepted in the Merchant Navy. Good morning, sir.'

He turned briskly to leave and barged into his close escort of nurses and students. Then he further increased their confusion by turning round to face me again.

'You are in the MNOPF?'

I blinked at him.

He rolled his eyes towards the ceiling. He felt his patience was being tried by talking to an idiot.

'The Merchant Navy Officers Pension Fund?' he said, enunciating each word slowly.

'Yes! I'm in the Pension Fund. I've been in it since 1950. I've been in it for thirty-three years.'

'Then you might just be entitled to a bit of your pension before you retire. Good day.'

A bit of my pension? At fifty-three? The thought stayed with me on the train journey all the way back to Scarborough. I had already accepted that I would be discharged from the Merchant Navy and would have to resort to earning my daily bread somehow, but with a chunk of Merchant Navy Pension assisting, I thought I would find something. My house was paid for, I had a few sound investments but there were still a few worries to think about.

I bless the day when Scottie, the MEA agent in Liverpool, enrolled me into the Union and the Pension Fund during my first week in the MN. Bless you, Scottie.

After a few days serious cogitation at home, a letter came, requesting I returned to the Shipping Federation in Hull. I felt they probably wanted me to be signed off officially and permanently.

During my spell at the Dreadnought in Greenwich, my dear wife had knitted me a dark red-polo neck jersey and I chose to wear it for the trip to Hull to show her my appreciation.

'I hope it brings you lots of luck,' she whispered in my ear as we set off. That jersey brought me tons of luck. Evidently the doctor in Hull needed to check my blood pressure for his own records so while my wife stayed outside in the car, my presence was required in the great man's surgery. However, taking off the dark red polo neck jersey presented a problem because the woolly collar was so tight and pulling it up over my head rubbed my eye lashes up the wrong way.

Blood pressure checked - Thank you Mister Jackman – See the Merchant Navy Union Man next door – Goodbye. NEXT!

I was out.

I pulled on my dark red polo neck jersey and was wiping my red eyes with my hankie before I went in to see the Union man, the Guardian Angel of those poor unfortunates that are doomed to serve their lives at sea.

He became quite distressed when he looked at me. 'Dear, dear, it's not as bad as all that. You have completed thirty-three years service and that entitles you to a full pension, Mr Jackman. It is a considerable sum of money every month, Mr Jackman.' He was still looking at me rubbing my eyes and thought I was crying because my Merchant Navy days were over. He didn't know I felt I wanted to jump up onto his desk and do the Highland Fling. The Pension was a godsend!

I remember laughing all the way back to Scarborough. Yet I regretted leaving the job that I loved so much.

I never had a wish to be a Chief Engineer. Bob Graham, 'Mac' Dryden, Jim Weir, Joe Cochran, Kevin O'Mahoney and many others were all highly competent Chief Engineers, great men to sail with and they never intruded in the duties or the responsibilities of the Second Engineer.

Had I become Chief, I know I would have been interfering in everything of a technical nature on board ship. I had been a 'fixer' of things since my childhood days and I had no wish to change, even at fifty-three.

But I was really going to miss working on board ships and meeting new lads. I would truly miss my life at sea. However the aforementioned S.S.M. that had pushed me into having my blood pressure checked in the first place came up trumps in the end with a telephone call a week later.

'Hello, Bob, Ron Murray here, sorry you're out of the MN now. We'll miss you. I've a job for you if you want it. It's an 80,000 ton oil tanker tied up in Terminus Quay in Glasgow, waiting to be converted into a sheep carrier. Would you like to stand by it for six weeks?'

A job! He then went on to inform me I was available for anything that floats as long as it floated between the Elbe and the Brest. I was now in the Coastal Trade. Life had just turned out to be great again.

This introduced me to the 'M.V. Earl of Skye'. She was old, tired and had been neglected in so many ways, yet I welcomed her like a girlfriend.

There were two other members already on board. There was Garry, a young second mate who was courting a girl in Edinburgh. He would slip away late on a Saturday afternoon and return about midday on the Sunday. This way he stood no chance of being found out by any superintendent who happened to pay us an unexpected visit.

However, as the weeks became months and superintendents visits became a regular routine at five o'clock every Friday, Garry would be well on his way to Edinburgh by five-thirty. His midday return on Sunday slowly increased to nearly midday on Monday.

It so happened, however, that one Monday about noon the Head Marine Superintendent walked on board our ship, looking for the aforementioned Garry.

'Right, Chief, have you seen the Second Mate? He's not in his cabin and he's not on deck anywhere.'

I was in working gear and had just come out of the engine room after checking the bilges.

'Garry? I'm not sure. He might have just nipped ashore to buy a couple of pizzas for our lunch.'

Who believes in miracles? In miracles? The door at the end of our alleyway opened and Garry appeared, carrying two pizzas! In our fifteen months together on board that old ship that was the only time Garry or anyone else ever came on board carrying two pizzas.

I know there are a multitude of strange things that happen on ships that border on the unbelievable, and that must be one of the strangest.

Our other crew member was Neil, an AB, and he was accompanied by a fat woman and a terrier dog. Garry and I seldom saw Neil or his companions from one week to another and neither did we want to.

Meantime, my wife Mary had taken a job in Scarborough, managing one of the Esplanade hotels for an elderly couple. We were under the impression my spell away from home would last a mere six weeks.

The hotelier was suddenly found to have cancer and Mary had to manage the hotel on her own with the holiday season just starting.

This left me pining away, Garry ran off to marry his lady love, I had no wish to meet Neil or his woman and I started talking to myself. I rarely saw the dog again, so perhaps they didn't let it out of their cabin where it just did what it had to do when Nature insisted.

I bought an old telly and watched every programme until my eyes started to go square, I spent long hours in the engine room overhauling everything that needed overhauling, I turned the main engine over once a day – in fact I did everything and anything to overcome intense boredom.

The old adage says it all. 'No man should go to sea if he can go to jail...'

Fifteen months passed and the idea of converting the 'Earl of Skye' from being an oil tanker to being a sheep carrier was discarded. She was to proceed to a breakers' yard in Korea to be scrapped.

Suddenly the old ship buzzed with activity. Garry was off, Neil and his woman were dumped on the quay with the dog and new people arrived with suitcases daily.

The sailing Chief quite rightly claimed the cabin I had occupied for the last fifteen months and I found myself in an assistant steward's cabin behind the bridge.

Clyde Marine Recruitment were in charge of supplying personnel. Their efficiency was proved when they discovered among the masses of small print involved that the new owners would finance everything for the journey to Korea but the ship's personnel would have to find their own way back to the United Kingdom! They had that contract changed in double quick time.

So I became Clyde Marine Recruitment's latest recruit and my future was secured in coasters.

A very long fourteen months finally ended when the 'Earl of Skye' left Terminus Quay in Glasgow on her last voyage to a breaker's yard in Korea.

I watched the old girl go. And I admit it, I was fifty-four years old and when she left the berth for her last voyage, I damn well felt like crying.

A PLAY

When high blood pressure demanded my departure from the Merchant Navy I joined the Coastal Trade where I met some strange characters and I sailed in some strange ships.

The 'MV Adventurer' fell into that category. She was small in every way and made trips around the North of Scotland when the weather allowed it or the Captain felt like it. We sat in the smoke-filled duty mess because it was the only place big enough on board that coaster where the five men could gather when off duty. I was the latest addition to this happy band of seafarers, but I was not a local and therefore I suffered some intense interrogation.

'You're from Kingussie?' It sounded like an accusation by the Mate while scrutinising the small print on the label of his can of beer.

'Aye.'

A few minutes passed before he spoke again. 'Quiet place, nothing to do in the winter. I'm from Stornoway. That's the place to live. Aye.'

Without raising his eyes from his can of beer or taking his pipe out of his face, the Captain nodded his head in agreement. 'Aye, that's the place to live. Nice people.' The Second Mate who was also part time-cook, looked at me and shook his head. It seemed he thought otherwise.

141

I opened beer can number four. 'I can tell you a wee story that involves Stornoway and Kingussie.'

'Aye?'

'Aye.

'Well, tell us then.'

'In Kingussie, in winter when the tourists have gone home, we find ways to pass the time. I was home on leave so I joined the Kingussie Drama Club. There were about ten of us and I began writing plays that went down quite well. I had written quite a few successful plays in the past. Dick, our leader, God bless him, was the local police sergeant, a jovial type that gave us a lot of encouragement. Then there was a beautiful lady called Anna, tall and slender, a newcomer from another village and her beauty took our audience's breath away. I could see Dick was particularly impressed by her. We had our rehearsals in the Victoria Hall in Kingussie, there were never any absentees or latecomers and everyone that took part in a play remembered their lines. One play I wrote had only two players, namely our stars, Dick and Anna. The play consisted of them arriving at a flat together, after receiving a surprise invitation to a party to be held there. They were to play the part of secret lovers and when they discovered the flat empty Dick swept Anna into his arms, as my script demanded, and kissed her. It was my play, I was the Director and I emphasised that all their kisses had to be long, hot and passionate. As I said, they were playing the part of established lovers. Audiences love that sort of thing. They tend to get overheated and their spectacles steam up, so at rehearsals I had them repeat the kisses more than a few times and I don't remember anyone having any objections. There were others in the group who wished to be stand-ins but my play only required one actor and one actress, the hot passionate variety.'

The Captain interrupted. 'Had they known each other before?'

'No, Captain. This beautiful Anna was a stranger to us. In the play they calmed themselves, got their breaths back and Dick, playing his part, suddenly found the door of the flat was locked. They started to panic a little. They were on the third floor and there's no fire escape or any way down, except through that door. There was a large camphorwood chest by the window. Dick opened it to find his own wife's dead body in it, and her throat had been cut. Then there was a loud banging at the door.'

'Police! Open up!'

That was the end of the play and my fellow seafarers nodded their approval. Then I told them that in the audience in our village hall there happened to be two talent scouts for SADA, the Scottish Amateur Drama Association. They informed us that we would be entered in the top five of the SADA Northern League and we were chosen to compete against Stornoway in their Theatre Hebridean, right in the middle of Stornoway.

Playing against Stornoway in the Eden Court Theatre in Inverness or the Norwood Theatre in Thurso might have given us a chance, but competing against the Stornoway Drama Club in Stornoway when the audience consisted entirely of Stornoway locals could handicap us a little.

Another difficulty would have been transporting our big camphorwood chest. It would take two of us to carry it to the ferry, and then carry it through the town to the Theatre Hebridean. Having to use a chest big enough to contain a human female body was the problem.

Why did the Scottish Amateur Drama Association not have our competition in a neutral ground like the Eden Court Theatre in Inverness? After all, it is the largest combined arts centre in the whole of Scotland and we had played there before.

However, Dick disentangled himself from the overheated Anna long enough to phone the Stage Manager of the Stornoway Drama Group.

'Och, aye,' he was told. 'Yes, lots of us have camphorwood chests, all sizes, no problem at all, at all. You can take your pick. We will find one that will suit you just fine. So dinna worry yersel.'

That was one worry less. Then I got called back to sea, a week before the Stornoway contest was due to start and problems began. Our new boy stage manager lost the artificial Yale lock I had made for the door and the camphorwood chest that their Drama Group presented us with, wasn't big enough to hold a cocker spaniel. The audience howled with laughter, stamped their feet and applauded like mad when Dick opened the tiny camphorwood chest, looked inside and screamed. 'It's my wife and she's dead.'

We didn't win.

When I came home from sea weeks later, Dick told me all about it. Then he breathed, 'Bob, I sure loved
     those rehearsals!'
     'Did you ever meet Anna again?'
     'No, Bob, she seems to have left the highlands entirely. And another thing: That daft Northern Gazette Newspaper wanted the play censored.'

I ALWAYS WIN SAHIB

We had completed tying up in Kidderpore
Dock in Calcutta. I had shed my sweat-
soaked boilersuit and showered when a
head popped round my cabin door'

"By Jehosophat! Bob, you dog it is you! I
heard you were on this bucket!"

"Soapy!" I was delighted to see Soapy
again. We had been shipmates and the closest of
friends on previous ships and perpetrators of
many a devilish ploy in the past. In the
Merchant Navy, one has shipmate, one has
friends and one has Department of Trade and
Industry acquaintances. To me, Soapy was a
shipmate, who had been through Oxford and
took an honours degree in ancient Greek before
deciding his future lay on the high seas.

"Yes, ancient Greek. I still say it was
damned silly of me but allow that I might sail on
Greek ships one day? Of course the crew would
have to be about fifteen hundred years old to
understand what I was saying and damn it all
old fruit, they are not so brisk at chipping off
rust or slapping paint on at that age, eh what?"

He was totally Dickensian in outlook and
manner, stocky and tweedy and looked as if he
should be sporting a monocle. He had a
background of ancestral homes, titled relatives,
squads of old family servants and he was reared
by a governess. Yet Soapy was just as

146

comfortable drinking with the working class in a back street pub as he would be with the aristocracy. He sailed as Second Mate. "The job's a doddle Bob. I'm not important enough to get giddy and I'm too high up to get trampled on." At a first meeting, he was often taken for an idiot. However, he proved to be an extremely competent ship's officer, as others quickly found out. His nickname came from his initials SOP.

"Where in the name of the wee man are you docked?" I asked him, handing him his first beer since he arrived three minutes earlier.

"Look out your port chum and you are looking straight at her, broadside on, straight across the jetty. I'll be able to wave beddy bye-byes to you tonight."

Two beers, or fifteen minutes later, we headed ashore and were ambushed by a 'garri-wallah'. A'garri is a horse drawn open coach similar to a landau and is a very common form of transport on Calcutta streets. The garri-wallah is generally the owner driver of this ostentatious speed machine and in this instance, ours was a five-foot stick insect with a black walnut for a head and he was bundled in an off-white bed sheet from his neck to his knees. We decided to travel by garri. The horse trotted for about twenty paces then settled down to a trembling walk. Neither whip nor curses, or jerking of the reins, increased the wretched creature's gait.

Eventually, we arrived in Chowringee, the great pulsing heart of Calcutta. Battalions of more bed-sheeted bodies with spindly legs and bare feet, were pushing their way along the crowded pavement. Much of the space on the pavements was occupied by native vendors, squatting under dazzling carbide lamps, illuminating their paltry wares. Myriads of green flies and mosquitoes were clustered round each light and 'Bombay canaries', a breed of slow flying tortoises, would cruise past our ears.

It was not a great distance from the docks, but it did take a long time. We were glad to finally disembark at the 'Prince's Night Club'

"OK how much? I asked, rupees at the ready.

"No Sahib'. He held up his hands to assist his refusal. "I wait for you.'

Since this was impinging on beer-drinking time, I relented and we entered the Prince's. Many beers later, we strolled quite steadily to the 'Bristol' with our garri-wallah following and continued imbibing until the clocks chimed the midnight hour. We decided to return home to our respective ships.

Our garri-wallah had waited for us against our wishes and India's answer to Red Rum trotted its twenty-five yards then limped on it's all four trembling legs, to reach our two ships.

"At last methinks we have arrived home, eh what?"

Soapy climbed down from the garri and stretched his limbs.

"Now old chap" I asked the garri-wallah. "How much do we owe you?"

"Eighty rupees, please Sahib."

"HOW MUCH?"

"Seventy rupees Sahib."

"Forget it. You don't get seventy rupees from us."

"Sixty rupees", he whined. "Last price."

"Soonow, tum char so beece wallah hi. Hum ay pisa nay do!"

The home made Hindustani immediately dropped the price to fifty and the haggling continued. To pay forty rupees in those far off days would have been quite generous; to pay fifty would have been stupid.

"Humm babu lagger", the garri-wallah threatened.

"Tiki, tum babu bollow eada row."

"What's the score old chap, what's happening?" Soapy was finding that his ancient Greek, like council house Glaswegian, was of little value in the Financial World of Indian Commerce. I explained that the haggling now stood at forty rupees and our irate stick insect was about to seek the assistance of the local constabulary.

"By Jove, you scoundrel; you won't get forty dingbats from us, damn sure you won't. Even thirty is too damn rich. So, when the constabulary arrives, bring them to me. That's my ship out there."

"And this ship here", I added, not to be left out.

The garri-wallah departed, wailing unpleasantries in his native tongue.

Six beers later, Soapy and I called it a day and he crossed the dock to his ship. I saw him wave 'goodbye' from the top of the gangway, before disappearing inside.

Next morning, the very humble garri-wallah appeared at my cabin door with tears in his eyes.

"Please Sahib, you speak forty rupees. Yes, forty rupees, very good price. I am bad. I try to cheat you. I sorry Sahib."

He looked such a miserable piece of humility I peeled three twenty rupee notes from my wad and handed them to him. He gasped as he took them and backed off, bowing and whispering "Ba-ote maribani, Sahib, ba-ote maribani."

He was still thanking me profusely as he backed down the alleyway and out onto the main deck.

Soapy appeared at beer time, one hour before lunch.

"Hey Bob, that garri-wallah chappie came on board my ship this morning with tears running down his face. I felt so damned sorry for him, I gave him sixty rupees."

KINGUSSIE

My wife Mary was born in the little village of Kingussie, one of the story-book types of villages that ladies love to read about in their magazines. It nestles in the Great Glen on the road between Perth and Inverness, in the lea of the mighty Cairngorm Mountains and overlooking one of Scotland's most beautiful rivers, the River Spey. The people who live in Kingussie are not just 'villagers.' I found them to be more like a family.

I was a Second Engineer Officer in the Merchant Navy sailing with Chinese companies and would often be away from home for eighteen months at a time. Mary was the Principal in the College of Domestic Science in Glasgow when we met and it was true love from that moment onwards. We were married in church in Perth and I think most of the villagers of Kingussie came to our wedding.

We rented our first house on West Terrace and shortly after that, bought our next house on Middle Terrace. The aged widower who owned 'Bracken Brae' was leaving to live with his son further south and sold us his lovely detached house, fully furnished, at a ridiculously low price because he knew both of us. He scorned all offers and advice from estate agents.

We paid his price through a Building Society, moved in, and I had to return to the

China coast run for another eighteen months for financial reasons.

Mary's mother and brother ran 'Barramore', a guest house in the village that overlooked the whole of the Spey Valley and Mary returned there to give a hand with the guests, leaving our 'Bracken Brae' empty.

Aviemore was being turned into an enormous tourist attraction and one of the top directors and his good lady approached Mary.

'Would you consider renting out your 'Bracken Brae,' to my wife and me? I am on the board of directors at Aviemore and I don't like resting too close to my place of work.'

So 'Bracken Brae' was rented out to Colonel Webber and his good lady. During their stay, the colonel, after asking Mary's permission, had the whole house rewired with extra connections though there was little wrong with the wiring in the house.

'Just a 'thank you' for such a low rent,' he explained.

When I came home after another eighteen month trip I was at peace with the world. The newsagent in the main street had been a sea captain in his younger days, but now long retired, and I would spend some time swopping stories with him when I bought my morning paper.

'I'll sell this shop to you one day, Bob.' It was always his parting remark and one day, on impulse, I bought his newsagents shop. It prospered from day one. Life in my wee shop was so much easier than working like a madman, over sixteen hours a day, charging up and down the China Coast on antiquated ships.

Mary run the Brownies and sometimes the whole pack of them would be in our shop at the same time, spending their pennies and asking questions. We always had time for everyone's children because we had no children of our own and both of us loved children.

Then one of 'the powers that be' in Church Circles requested I give a talk to the Cubs in the church hall, a talk about the sea.

'Yes, certainly, but can I have a blackboard?'

When it came to the appointed hour, I drove my car down Spey Street behind the houses, then round the corner to the church hall at the required time, a mere two minute journey, unobserved by anyone, and dressed in my full Merchant Navy uniform. Eyes would have widened and there would have been interruptions and delays had I walked to the Church Hall because many only thought of me as Bob the Newsagent.

I entered the hall and the cubs now found themselves facing a Senior Naval Officer of the Merchant Navy.

I took over the class from the wide-eyed young Cub Mistress who also saw me in a very different light. It's great what a navy uniform can do.

So I turned to the class and wrote on the

blackboard in large block capital letters, the words:

ACCIDENTS DON'T HAPPEN.

I could hear their murmurings behind me as they queried my statement so I waited a moment before turning round to observe their reactions. Then I wrote,

ACCIDENTS ARE CAUSED.

From then, they listened to every word I said and they longed for more. My talks to the cubs became a regular event and I loved it just as much as they did and their numbers increased. Their eyes and their minds were opened to the world outside Kingussie. I talked about engines, ships, peoples and places and they listened to every word. I explained why learning things were necessary to be a success in the world and that was why school was so important.

Time passed and in the summer months tourists came in their hundreds and the village prospered from their visits. They found the locals to be very friendly and easy to talk with.

I remember when the Very Reverend Donald Caskie became the minister in our church. His book, 'The Tartan Pimpernel', told of his life in occupied France helping British prisoners of war to escape to Spain, but he diluted his telling of the heinous tortures the Nazis put him through to confess how they escaped. He never told them. His tortures were told in detail in books written by other people who were in France with him.

Iain Kaye, the poet, after his whole life in the army, retired to Kingussie and continued to write poems. I kept a few of his books in the shop to sell to customers and if I sold one I would tell the customer that I could have Mr Iain Kaye's autograph on it, within the hour. The noble Iain Kaye had hung up all his medals in a picture frame on his sitting room wall and now drove the village dustcart. If he saw a copy of his book lying flat in my shop window, it was our signal he was needed for a book-signing.

We had a new Catholic Priest, a Father Kennedy, who came to the village from parts unknown and he and our minister, the Reverend Sidney McEwan, became good friends.

I remember one summer during a heat wave when the River Spey had dwindled down to being little more than a trickling stream. In those conditions, trout could see an angler coming from fifty yards away and consequently no one had caught a trout in weeks.

One morning the priest came into my shop.

'Bob,' he asked pensively, 'You are a fisherman. Well, I'm having a very important guest coming to visit me tomorrow, a bishop in fact, and I've been praising the wonders and virtues of everyone and everything. I told him what a wonderful place Kingussie is and about the River Spey with all its trout. May I ask, Bob, do you think you could catch two trout for me, just to impress the bishop tomorrow?'

In the Highlands we don't say 'no' to impossible requests without at least attempting something. I didn't have much hope when I made my way down to the Spey late that evening but I was flabbergasted when I caught four lovely trout, two three-quarter pounders and two a little larger.

It was dark when I stopped at the priest's house on my weary way home and knocked on his housekeeper's door. When she appeared in dressing gown and curlers I held up the trout.

'Och, it's yersel, Bob. My, yer troot are real bonny.'

'Aye, Mrs Anderson. Father Kennedy asked me to get him two trout for tomorrow, but he didn't say what size he wanted so I just got him two of each.'

I left her in the doorway holding the four trout, standing with her mouth open, admiring them. I sometimes wonder if the Good Lord had given me a helping hand that night.

We had a Drill Hall in the village where soldiers were often stationed to be taught about survival in mountainous areas. On one occasion, many years ago, a dozen Highland Light Infantry arrived with a Sergeant Cawder and met our new local police sergeant, Dick Smith. Dick was a hefty build of a man with a big smile for everyone and he had been requested to take the soldiers up into the Cairngorms on a survival course.

The soldiers were tough, brittle Glasgow men and they looked upon Dick quite disdainfully when they met him. They judged him to be a village yokel that had never seen a tram car.

The army sergeant pursed his lips and asked Dick. 'Right, Police Sergeant Smith, it's now two o'clock, we have had a lunch, so when shall we begin this mountain survival course that you are going to teach us all about?'

'I think if we all meet in the bar of the Duke of Gordon Hotel at, say, seven o'clock tonight? I don't want to be too hard on you if it's your first time in the mountains.'

The soldiers looked at each other in disbelief then their sergeant spoke with a dry smile on his lips. 'I don't think you would be hard on us, Police Sergeant Smith. In fact, I don't think you could be hard on us. We'll meet you outside the Duke of Gordon Hotel at seven o'clock tonight.'

So, the story goes, they met at the appointed hour outside the hotel, fully equipped for their lessons on survival in mountainous terrain and set off up the village's Town Clock Brae, towards Craig Beg. After three hours plodding uphill, Dick stopped them and they slumped down into the heather, exhausted.

'Aye, that wasn't too bad at all,' Dick smiled. 'Ye have done quite well but it's getting to be a wee bit too dark to walk without lighting. So, Sergeant Cawder would you shine your torch on this?' Dick produced a litre bottle of Scotch and a pen. 'Just write yer name on the label, that's all I'm asking.'

After a moment's hesitation the sergeant scribbled his name on the label.

Dick held out the bottle and the pen to a soldier standing close by watching the proceedings.

'What's your name, laddie?'

'Carmichael. Hughie Carmichael.'

'Well, Hughie Carmichael, would you oblige me by writing your name on the label o' this bottle?'

So Private Carmichael duly wrote his name beside his sergeant's name and Dick replaced the bottle in his haversack. 'Aye. That's just fine.'

Within fifteen minutes they were all sound asleep in the heather, glad for the opportunity to try and rest their aching muscles.

The dawn light was edging down Craig Beg, touching the tops of higher peaks when Dick wakened the sergeant and his men. A small herd of stags in the distance watched them closely.

The soldiers were beginning to realise that this village policeman was a tougher man than they first thought. The long climb up the steep slope through thick heather had not tired him in any way that they could see and he was ready to start again.

'Right, laddies, biscuits and water for breakfast; we have a long way to go. If your water flask is empty, fill it.'

'And where do you expect us to find water up here?'

Dick smiled. 'You see these staggies over yonder? They can always find the little streams running through the heather. They are drinking clear mountain water now. So go and fill your flasks.'

Dick patiently waited twenty minutes for them to be ready then he marched them at a smart pace uphill to the high plateau on top of Craigellachie on the far side of Loch Gynack.

The soldiers' legs were aching with fatigue and it showed on their faces.

Suddenly Dick stopped and looked around. He looked one way, then another, then back the way they had come.

The soldiers began muttering. 'The bugger's got us lost.'

'He hasn't a bliddy clue where we are.'

'We'll never find our way back.'

Dick turned and faced them. 'Hughie, would you please walk a bit further on until I tell you to stop? Aye, that way, keep going. That's good, that's far enough. Go a bit more to the left. Good. Now what is lying at your feet?'

Hughie parted the heather and picked a litre bottle of whisky. He brought it back to them. 'It's got my signature on it, sergeant, and yours as well.'

Not a sound as they looked at their names on the bottle.

Dick nodded. 'When you were sleeping...'

The army sergeant looked at him. 'You came here! You walked for an hour in total darkness, planted the bottle in the heather and walked all the way back. Over two hours through thick heather in these mountains in the dark on your own.....'

Dick interrupted him. 'Och, let's say that was your first lesson and you did well. I think you have all earned a wee dram.' He uncorked the bottle. 'And I think maybe you have all learned your first lesson, lads, and I didna hurt ye at all, now, did I?' He handed the bottle to Sergeant Cawder. 'And a wee dram before breakfast will no' hurt ye either.'

THREE MIRACLES

Christmas? It's a great excuse for a party, and nothing else. It's a load of blooming rubbish, a chance for adults to get drunk and kids to get toys. I tell you, it's nothing else.' Our Sparky thumped his fist on our smoke-room bar to emphasize his remarks and looked around to see if anyone would contradict him.

We looked at each other to consider his words then our bold Fourth Engineer, Jimmy Hudson, spoke up in his broad Glasgow voice.

`It might be that way, aye, ye might be right, but whether ye are right or wrong, does it dae anybody any harm? If it doesn't dae anybody any harm, why knock it?'

There were eight of us sprawled around in the 'Ardmore's' smoke-room, everyone from Captain Hooper to the deck cadet Flynn and it was Christmas Eve.

Captain Hooper was as placid and tolerant as a Church of Scotland minister and he seldom took part in any beer-soaked discussions that rose in our smoke-room. He drank clear lemonade, had a book on his lap and his presence was a calming influence to us all.

But on this occasion, Sparky was not to be calmed. 'It's a load of rubbish, all this religious stuff, and all these miracles. Whoever saw a miracle? Come on. Whoever even heard of a miracle that happened when they were there? C'mon, speak up, any of you.'

Captain Hooper closed his book and smiled. 'I'll speak up, Sparky. I will tell you of a miracle.'

Sparky looked at all our faces for a moment, but we chose to remain silent. We don't argue with Captains.

'Tell us about your miracle, Captain.'

We were sitting with him round a coffee table and those at the bar moved over to join us.

He filled his pipe, lit it and settled himself, but I could see he was debating internally whether to tell us or not.

Then he began: 'My childhood years were spent in a poor orphanage called 'St Arlans.' Then when I was fifteen, I took a job in a shop that organised worldwide holiday cruises and probably that gave me the urge to go and see the world. When I was seventeen a shipping company had come under new owners and wanted deck apprentices so I applied and I was one of the deck apprentices chosen. The new owners were a family that looked upon shipping as a great source of interest and pleasure and when any of their ships came into the UK they came to visit those on board.'

He took his pipe out of his mouth and pointed it at each of us in turn. 'Ship owners? Some ship owners hardly ever know what the inside of a ship's cabin looks like. But this family was different. We were in Tilbury and we were ready to sail next morning when the owner and his wife came to wish us all a happy trip. His dear wife heard the Chief Engineer had his wife on board and went to pay her a visit. She didn't like the curtains on the windows in the Chief's cabin so the two ladies, the owner's wife and Chief's wife, went ashore and had new curtains made. It was four days before we sailed, held up because the owner's wife said the Chiefs cabin needed new curtains. Four days! Those were the type of people who now owned the company.'

We all looked at each other, wondering what to believe. But Captain Hooper was a gentleman, the type of fellow who would never tell lies about anything, whatever the cost.

`OK, Captain, tell us about the miracle,' I asked him softly.

`Yes, Bob. I was seventeen and I fell down the hatch. We were in Mobile in Alabama, the cargo was all discharged and I fell from the main deck to the bottom of number two hold. I was pronounced dead. They said I was dead because of the distance I had fallen – I couldn't possibly be alive, by anyone's reckoning. But the captain phoned for an ambulance, then phoned the ship-owner. Nearly every bone in my body was broken but because my heart still had a slight tick they put me into the emergency department of the local infirmary. I think I oozed so much blood on to the operating table it streamed off the end and made a puddle on the floor. They stitched up every wound that was pouring blood until finally they came to a halt. While they were working on me I could hear them muttering:

'Poor bastard, this is a waste of time,' and `he ain't in any pain, thank Gawd.'

But after a long silence another voice came to me, a voice that was different from the others, a soft voice. It said, 'You shall survive this, my son, you shall survive.'

`And it wasn't just another doctor or nurse that was speaking?' Sparky butted in.

`No, Sparky. When any of the medical staff spoke there were other sounds, sounds of people moving and things like that, but when that one voice spoke, it was during a long silky silence. I felt I was no longer in that hospital and that I had been moved somewhere. What I thought was a matter of hours proved to be a matter of weeks.'

He leaned forward, knocked the ash out of his pipe and looked around at our faces for a moment. He was unused to talking so much.

`Briefly, they just kept me alive until my strength came back and then began the long business of repairing my broken bones. One of the company's office staff was sent out to make sure I had everything I needed, report my progress to our ship owner and pay all the American medical bills, etcetera. Ten months later, I was fit enough to be flown back to the UK to the Dreadnought with a doctor beside me.' He paused. 'All this talking is making me thirsty.'

Seven beers and a lemonade appeared at the table by the time he had filled his pipe and lit it.

`Anyway, in the Dreadnought I always had lots of visitors and they brought me books. When I had tired of detective stories, big Ted Oddy began to bring me nautical class books. Then I ended up with a teacher from the Nautical College for two hours a day. It was twenty-two months before I was fit enough to join a ship. With all this tuition being pumped into me I rose quickly in the ranks. I took my Master's Certificate at twenty-five and sailed as Captain when I was twenty-six.'

He looked around at our faces for a moment, and then rose to leave. 'I think I have talked enough for one day, gentlemen, thanks for the drink.'

`Your miracle was surviving the fall into the hold, Captain, and everybody thought you were dead? That was your miracle?' Sparky always liked to get his facts right.

The Captain stopped by the smoke room door. 'The miracle was that voice. The voice that spoke in an absolute silence: 'you shall survive this, my son,' so clearly when others had repeatedly pronounced me dead. To me, that was a miracle. So, good night, gentlemen, and with that thought in mind, I hope you sleep well.'

There was a chorus of 'good nights' from all of us.

He closed the door behind him and the smoke room suddenly seemed so quiet and empty.

Eventually our Sparky muttered,' I still don't believe in miracles. I mean, even if the

Captain did hear the voice it was probably in his imagination.'

'There are so many things happen that we can't explain,' Danny, our Chief Steward muttered, as he ran the tip of his finger slowly round the top of his beer bottle.

'A miracle?' Sparky spread his arms wide and raised his eyes to look at the deck head above him. 'On Christmas Eve, we always have miracles. Christmas is a time for fairy tales and lots of beer.'

'It's also a good time for a smack in the mouth,' Jimmy muttered, showing Sparky his clenched fist.

I have often heard remarks and threats like that in my forty years in the Merchant Navy, tons of them, but I don't ever recall seeing anything that could be called a fight.

Danny scratched the back of his head and spoke aloud. 'Well, I've got something to tell you about miracles. Are you going to listen?'

We agreed to listen.

He sighed, and then began. 'I was in a Shell tanker back in 1958 and we were anchored outside Jeddah in the Persian Gulf. It was a couple of days before Christmas.'

'Oh, aye, here we go again.' Sparky shook his head in mock exasperation.

'Watch it!' Jimmy warned him.

Sparky snorted, but he did shut up.

Danny looked at the pair of them, and then continued. 'We had two deck cadets, Irish lads, and Ginger, the older of the two, could shin up ropes and ladders like a startled monkey. Paddy was the quiet one, quiet but brainy. They paid me a visit to ask for a couple of bed sheets out the store room. Well, to make a long story longer, they had borrowed the Captain's wife's long hair piece. It came right down on to her shoulders. Ginger was going to dress himself up in the bed clothes, wear the hair piece and climb up the after mast to the crosstree. Paddy would turn the Aldis lamp on him and Ginger would recite stuff from the bible.'

Sparky and Jimmy were now engrossed in the story and, like the rest of us, they sat quietly.

`Well, go on. What happened? What was the miracle?'

Danny was quiet for a moment, then continued. 'Paddy ran into the smoke room and shouted; 'Come and see this!' So we went outside and the figure we saw was in full view in the spotlight on the after mast crosstree. The robes and the hair moved in the breeze and the arms were outstretched. We could hear his voice and it was as if he was quoting straight from the bible but he wasn't holding a bible.'

I remember Danny looking at us as he spoke. 'The voice had carried down from the crosstree to us, every word clear. But the Aldis lamp suddenly went out for no reason.'

He was starting to shake a little and on an impulse, I reached over the bar and poured a large Scotch. He sat with it on the table before him, and then continued with his story.

`Ginger and Paddy came into the smoke room together, shouting at each other. Then Ginger told us what he was shouting about. He told us the bed sheets got tangled round his feet when he tried to climb the ladder up the mast so he went into the seamen's quarters for a piece of string or rope to hold the sheets up a bit. The crew were in a great mood so they laughed at him in his bed sheets and plied him with a few large whiskies. Once he got the whiskies, he was in no fit state to go up the mast. So who was the figure in the crosstrees who recited the bible?' Danny looked at us. 'I confirmed all this with the crew. Ginger never went up the mast so who was the figure that appeared on the cross tree? Who was the figure that spoke bits of bible stuff?'

We were all silent. Then Jimmy spoke. 'Well, that was two miracles. We all go along wi' that? Agreed? Well, I am going to top both these miracles. Because I can tell you of a third miracle, gentlemen that happened here today.'

We looked at each other, perplexed.

`A third miracle?'

`Aye,' Jimmy stood up and pointed a finger at Sparky. 'I just got this twit to pay for that last round of beers. That, to me, was the greatest miracle of all!'

THE POETRY BUG

It happens. You have filled in the log book, made up the work book, added a couple of items to the stores list and written half a page to the wife. The Fourth is on watch, the Third is asleep and the Fiver is somewhere working on his winches. Confronted with the blank pages of a writing pad in front of you and a ball point pen in your sweaty grip, you can be attacked by 'The Poetry Bug.'

For example:

The Lord made the seas and the winds,
And fools made seafaring their lives,
So the Lord, in His wisdom,
Took some Angels and blessed them
And gave them to seamen for wives.

Or again, in a different mood:

I touch a leg with my fingertips,
And feel my heartbeat quicken.
I raise a breast to my hungry lips.
Oh! How I love fried chicken.

I gathered my poems into a book I called 'Diverse Verses.'

People ashore often ask me; 'How long were you at sea, Bob, and were you ever in a storm?' Typhoon 'WANDA' caught us in the Formosa Straits in 1956. It was travelling from east to west when we were caught by a wind force of two hundred miles an hour. We were going north so the Captain decided we would go up the Formosa Straits and be partly sheltered by the land. But WANDA turned and met us head on......

WANDA

I was forty-one years at sea and, yes, I've been in storms,
I was umpteen years on the China Coast where typhoons were the norm
And what's a big typhoon like? Well, according to Statistics,
The biggest one was 'Wanda' back in 1956.

Yes, the biggest one was Wanda and I recall the day she found us,
Behind the island of Formosa, with rocks and reefs around us.
The day turned black as pitch, the wind increased in force,
So we upped the engines to maximum to try to keep us on our course.

Soon a God Almighty shaking and a continuous thunder clap
Made the engines scream in agony like wild beasts in a trap,

Merchant Navy – What A Life

*We went soaring to the Heavens and twisting as
we fell,
And were pounded by a demon intent on sending
us to Hell.*

*From the depths of all damnation, this mad
Satanic power,
This wind that shrieked in fury at two hundred
miles an hour
This wind that shrieked in fury and scoured the
paint off steel,
Danced our ship around in circles in a wild
abandoned reel.*

*Three days and nights of anxiety expecting to 'go
under',
Three days of unhallowed darkness in a roar of
constant thunder,
Stupefied with the lack of sleep and our body's
need for nourishment,
Tell us, God, what have we done to deserve this
kind of punishment?*

*On the morning of the fourth day, the sea was
quite serene,
The breeze blew very gently where the lifeboats
once had been.
Lifejackets gone, lifebelts gone and the Captain
let us know,
We were now five miles behind where we were
four days ago.*

Yes, I was forty years at sea and yes, I've been in storms,
With umpteen years on the China Coast where typhoons were the norm,
And what's a big typhoon like? Well, according to statistics,
The biggest one was 'WANDA' back in 1956.

***

Typhoons hit Hong Kong and Kowloon about every six to ten years and some are called 'WANDA'. In our 'WANDA' of 1956 the destruction to the city was enormous where the winds faded to a mere one hundred and seventy miles per hour and waves six foot deep roared up Nathan Road on the Kowloon side as far as 'The Bamboo Bar.'

When high blood pressure shifted me from deep sea vessels to the coastal trade I met some heroes there. One ship was just an old relic of a job with a cramped engine room and a clapped out engine that clattered and rattled and required a lot of watching.

Dougie was the cook, steward, AB and Chief Dishwasher in a galley as big as a telephone box. He was a wee man that never seemed to go to bed or talk about his home or family. I don't think he had a home. I remember him telling me this:

HOW DO YOU JUDGE MEN, CHIEF?

*I*t was four bells on the midnight watch, or 2am to you,
And I'd come up from 'down below' to make myself a brew.
I found Dougie in the duty mess, he'd already made the tea,
So I parked my weary backside while he poured a cup for me.

Now Dougie was an 'AB' as tough as army boots,
Old and kind and honest and proud of his Glasgow roots,
Right through the war on the seven seas with U-boats in contention.
But never a word on all he'd seen, never a bliddy mention.

Aye, Dougie was a quiet man, he'd never much to tell,
But sometimes on a lonely ship it's good to talk a spell.
'We were heading for the Firth o' Clyde, I can see it now,
When we were passed by a Spanish ship, a mile off our port bow.'

'An hour went by, we'd changed the watch and I had gone below,

173

When my 'oppo' saw, dead line astern, a fiery
orange glow.
'Good God' he cried. 'The Spanish ship!' Mater
and Mate agreed.
'Turn this bloody ship around and let us have
some speed.'

'Now hear me, Chief, I don't tell lies and I'm not
lying now.
But I was frightened stiff that night – the sweat
was on my brow.
We battered on towards that glow and rolling in
the swell,
And all around as black as pitch, as black as the
hounds of Hell.'

'Well, we drew near, we saw her burn, a solid
mass of fire,
Her midship plates were smoking red, the bridge
a funeral pyre.
'We want volunteers to man a boat!' We heard the
Mate's command.
'And God knows why I did it, Chief, but I put up
my hand.'

'It took four of us to man the oars and the Second
Mate to steer her,
But each wave nearly coup'd us and the
Spaniard seemed no nearer.
We pulled our bliddy guts out, Chief, the going
was that hard,
We bent the oars, we broke our backs we fought
for every yard.'

Merchant Navy – What A Life

We made it to the Spaniard's bow where panicky
voices roared,
Then they were in the sea with us and we're
hauling them on board.
Back to pulling our guts out, Chief, ignoring the
bloody pain.
'Our Father which art in Heaven, Oh hallowed be
Thy name.'

'Back to the rowing, I don't know how, and the
Captain shouted 'Fine!'
We've lowered the boat on the other side, you can
tow it close behind.
There's lots of men on the poop deck aft, destined
for Kingdom Come,
So once again we took the oars, mentally and
physically numb.'

A mass of blisters on both my hands and most of
them had burst.
Shoulders and arms with a million pains and I
was not the worst.
Yet once again we went there and back – the
Spanish ship was going,
C'mon you bastards, pull you bastards, keep up
with that rowing.'

Here, Dougie stopped, his tea stone cold, his cup
in a vice like grip,
And in his mind he was seeing again the burning
Spanish ship.'
'Twenty-nine men we saved that night, every
member of her crew.

*We did the best we could, Chief, what more could
we do?'*

*'But here's a bit to make you laugh, you're sure to
appreciate,
They gave an award to each AB and one to the
Second Mate.
To the five of us who manned the boat to save
those Spanish men,
The Second mate got a ten pound note and we got
seven pounds ten.*

*How do you judge men, Chief, how do you deal
with bunkum?
The Income Tax took two pounds ten and called it
'Unearned Income.'*

*****

This was Dougie's story and he told it as
he remembered it. All I did was make it rhyme.
He was truly a man high on the list of the
Merchant Navy Heroes I write about.

THE GOLD AND THE PURPLE

*E*ngineers wear purple on the edge of their
gold braid,
*It was a Queen's demand it be there, and
this is what she said,
'Those silent and modest heroes, for the courage
they displayed,*

Merchant Navy – What A Life

Will wear the Royal Purple on the edge of their gold braid.'

*Once officers were officers, engine and deck quite equal,
But someone on the deck side erred with a terrifying sequel.
A collision with an iceberg by a ship they called 'Titanic',
Then the bungling at the lifeboats, the incompetence, the panic.*

*The survivors told the story and they are the ones who know,
Of the Engineers on board that ship who chose to 'go below',
To die in that Hell in the engine room, running the pumps and engines,
To stay the final outcome, to delay the cruel sea's vengeance.*

*Not for them the lifeboats and the chance they might survive,
They knew what their fate would be when 'Titanic' took her dive.
Burning coals and roaring steam and death when boilers burst,
The Engineers stayed on duty when Hell was at its worst.*

So Engineers wear purple on the edge of their gold braid,
It was a Queen's demand it be there, and this is what she said.
'Those silent and modest heroes, for the courage they displayed,
Will wear the Royal Purple on the edge of their gold braid.'

HOW COMPANIES DIFFER

In companies registered in Hong Kong, companies such as Williamson, Douglas and Mullion, the crew consisted of a mere six British officers, six Chinese officers and a Chinese crew. Contracts were usually for eighteen months to two years long and the ships were far from new.

Generally, shore side repair work was carried out in Hong Kong by the Hong Kong and Whampoa Repair Yard whose repairs and maintenance were far from satisfactory unless closely supervised by the ship's staff - and ship's staff in many cases were too eager to 'have a break' in the naval paradise of Hong Kong.

I was once involved in Hui Ying of Cosmo Dock Repair Yard being given the opportunity to do our overhauls and repairs and other companies followed. We never regretted it.

Conditions being what they were or could be, meant you were financially rewarded for your efforts and being outside the UK during a financial year meant you were free of UK income tax. This meant a trip to the Hong Kong Tax Office in Ice House Street where one's eighteen month Hong Kong income tax could be paid with the loose change in one's pocket.

It could be a life of hard graft and sweated labour but the rewards were truly worth it. And when the agonies of hard work improved the ship's performance the financial rewards remained high, or even increased. I can recall receiving a quiet £400 bonus on two occasions and I am sure others did too.

Being at home after an eighteen month trip could tempt me to do a short trip on a coaster or a similar vessel for any number of reasons.

Clyde Marine Recruitment springs to mind. 'Bob, a coaster that's a diving platform needs a chief engineer in a hurry. Just for today, their Chief hasn't turned up. She's in the Humber.'

I drove down from my home town of Scarborough, found the ship, parked the car at the bottom of the gangway and the Captain was waiting at the top of the gangway.

`Mr Jackman, Chief Engineer? Our Mr Roberts arrived fifteen minutes ago. You came by train from Inverness? Good. Here's a cheque to cover your expenses.'

"My car........'

`Your car? I don't see any cars about here.' (My car was less than ten yards below his nose.) He shook my hand and smiled. 'Thank you and good-bye, Sir.'

He left me standing on deck with a £100 cheque in my hand and £100 was quite a good wage for a two hour drive in 1969.

I had a spell as stand-by Second Engineer on the 'Scottish Prince' in 1965 and joined before 8am. The second's cabin was in darkness, there was no one else about so I left my hold-all and my coat in the duty mess and went for a walk round the engine room.

Everything was quite clean, but I could see quite a lot of faults that would need putting right. An old donkeyman was sitting on a box with his back against the main engine and his boots flat against the silently running Allan steam generator. He stood up to let me pass, we said a few polite words to each other to establish who I was, and then he walked over to flash up the Cochran boiler by hand.

`Doesn't it work on automatic?'

He pursed his lips and shook his head. 'Never has done.'

Forty-five minutes later it was working on automatic and I stayed another forty-five to make sure it was running satisfactorily. Meantime, I made a tour of the engine room and mentally noted quite a few jobs that would need doing, but assumed they would be on the Second's work list.

Still no sign of the Second I was relieving, his cabin was still in darkness and I heard the sound of cutlery and dishes rattling in the next alleyway. I had found the pantry.

`Cup of coffee, please.'

So I was handed a mug of coffee with some sugar, some milk and a lot of bored indifference and I made my way to the duty mess.

Time marched on and there was suddenly a squad of workers on board, heading for the engine room and a timorous little gentleman in Chief Engineer's uniform appeared, looked at me and disappeared again. Things had started to move, including my blood pressure.

When the timorous little gentleman appeared again, he started talking non-stop as he handed me a sheet of paper. It was the sleeping Second Engineer's list for jobs that needed doing by ship staff.

Pathetic!

I was given the spare cabin, so I dumped my gear, put on a boiler suit and found the Third, Fourth, Fifth Engineers sitting in the smoke room in uniform. Seven minutes later they were in the engine room in boiler suits.

Evidently, ship's staff don't work in UK ports in this company. It would seem that ships staff don't work in any ports in this company but this group were quite happy to work on jobs that needed doing.

We came out of the engine room just before noon and I went to see if the Second Engineer was alive. I found him in his cabin, in his underpants, knocking back beers with the ship's carpenter.

How companies differ.

F W E*

These are memories of places I have been to, ships I have sailed on, but most of all, they are memories of the lads I have sailed with during my forty years in the Merchant Navy.

It's a special breed of man that leaves a wife and kids for months on end and doesn't know if his next trip is going to be a pleasure cruise or a nightmare.

On a pleasure cruise where everything runs smoothly, the seas are calm and the food is excellent; it is great to look back on. But a trip where everything went haywire, you are battered from one force ten to another and the food is lousy, it still had its moments. It is all part of a life that we seafarers have loved and it's hard when you ring 'Finished with Engines' for the last time ever.

Amen.

Bob Jackman, 2nd Engineer

For the benefit of those readers not accustomed to the sea, FWE stands for "Finished with Engines". When finished coming alongside a berth, the Mate on the bridge rings this on the telegraph and the Engineer on watch answers and shuts down the main engines.

FINALE

'Parting is such sweet sorrow'
Is the gospel of Shakespeareans,
But I'm so old I differ,
And quote my own experience.
I'm old, tired and broken hearted,
My turn has come – don't doubt it.
Ships and I have long last parted,
There's damn all sweet about it.

SHIPS 1950 — 1990

Marjata 1950;
Megna 1951;
City of Chester 1953;
City of Lille 1954;
City of Poona 1956;
City of Bath 1957;
City of Swansea 1957;
Inchmull 1959;
Kirtondyke 1960;
Inchstuart 1960;
Inchstaffa 1962;
Ardmore 1962;
Ardtara 1964;
Scottish Prince 1965;
Cyprian Prince 1965;
African Prince 1965;
Rowanmore 1965;
Obuasi 1966;
Ribot 1966;
Quartz 1970;
Cumbernauld1971;
Cape Race 1974;
Cape Howe 1975;
Baron Dunmore1976;
Cape Howe 1977;
Cape Sable 1977;
Ikan Bilis 1978;
Baron Belhaven 1979;
Baron Maclay 1979;
Cape Leeuwin 1980;
Cape Race 1980;
Baron Belhaven 1981;
Baron Napier 1981;
Baron Pentland 1982;
Otterburn 1985;
Bon Accord 1989;
Hebridean Princess 1990.

Interspaced with an assortment of tugs, motorised barges, unnamed tiny coasters, twenty-four hour jobs, 'standing by' others, vessels that had faults that baffled repair yards - the list is enormous.

The Chief I relieved on one scrap yard of a coaster was a nervous wreck, fully dressed, and wearing a lifejacket. Electricity came from a one cylinder horizontal diesel generator that rattled and clattered. There were two such generators,

but the second one was broken beyond repair and there were no spare parts.
More to follow? No. No more.

Merchant Navy – What A Life

Printed in Great Britain
by Amazon